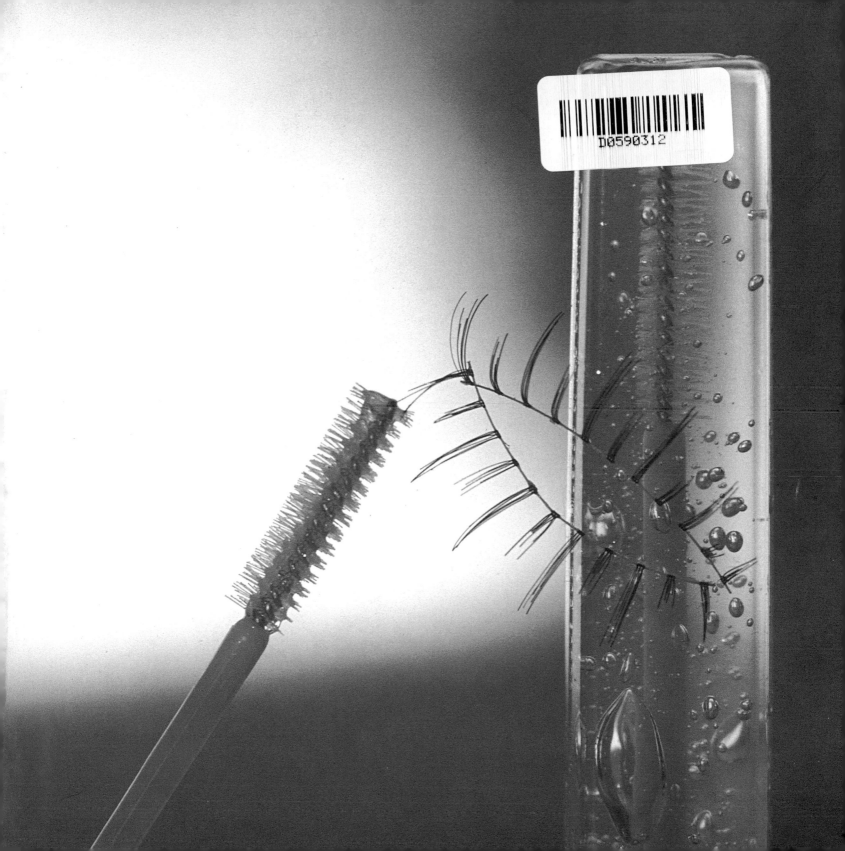

D0590312

ESSENTIAL
BEAUTY

For Russ and Emily

First published in Great Britain in 1995 by
The Boots Company PLC Nottingham England

Typeset by J&A Artwork Ltd
Printed and bound in Great Britain by BPC Hazell Books Ltd,
a member of the British Printing Company Ltd
Print Management by The Finnemore & Field Group of Companies
Litho Origination by Alan Graphic, Watford, Herts ·

ISBN 1-873116-02-0

Note from the Publisher
Any information given in *Essential Beauty* is not intended to be taken as a replacement for
medical advice. Any person with a condition requiring medical attention should consult a
qualified medical practitioner or suitable therapist.

INTRODUCTION

N°7 ESSENTIAL BEAUTY

Today's woman wants honest, hard-working beauty products and no-nonsense advice. As skincare, haircare and make-up formulations become increasingly diverse and sophisticated, the ways in which we are using cosmetics are also changing.

The aim of **N°7 Essential Beauty** is to bring you details of the new treatments and the best techniques in a fresh, visually-stimulating format. Here you will discover everything you need to know to create and maintain a great skin, from recognising your skin's cleansing and moisturising needs (which alter more frequently than you might think) to essential anti skin-ageing strategies.

A comprehensive guide to choosing the right make-up shades for your colouring, and the look for the occasion, is teamed with lots of application ideas for the latest make-up textures.

Bodycare is a surefire way to boost self-esteem and to impart a sense of well-being. Whether you want to fight cellulite, lose a few inches or counteract the effects of stress, I hope you will find a wealth of ideas in this section that can be slotted into even the busiest schedule.

Frizzy, fine, dry, damaged, greasy, or simply beautiful, your hair deserves a little love and attention. You can find problem-solving and styling suggestions throughout the haircare chapter.

N°7 Essential Beauty has been designed so that you can dip in and out of each page and each chapter. I hope you will find it helpful, informative and entertaining.

Chrissie Painell

CONTENTS

Recognising your genetically-determined skin type is the first step towards improving and maintaining a great skin. But it's only part of the story. Your skin is also affected by other factors such as by your age, the changing seasons, exposure to the elements, smoking and the environment. Even stress or soap and water can upset your skin's equilibrium. Make the regular re-evaluation of your skin's needs part of your overall skincare regime.

NORMAL SKIN Generally well-behaved, normal skin has an even texture and a bloom to it. Use gentle cleansers and avoid soap which disrupts the acid mantle. Toners which contain alcohol should also be avoided because of their tendency to dry the skin. Apply a moisturiser daily. The environment is almost always drier than your skin and will rob it of moisture if you don't protect your complexion.

DRY SKIN Naturally dry skin does not produce enough sebum, the skin's lubricating oil. Sebum production decreases as we age.

Dehydrated skin is temporarily dry as a result of exposure to the sun, cold, wind, central heating, and smoking, or possibly as a result of the constant use of soap, which can break down the skin's lipids (natural oils). Dehydrated skin feels tight and drawn and when you smile you may be able to see fine lines or wrinkles that are not usually present. Dry skin can look thin and papery, and is also prone to broken veins. Use a rich, creamy cleanser and check that your toner is alcohol-free. You need deeply moisturising protective daycare and will benefit from a 12 hour hydrator. Use an enriched, nourishing night cream, too.

OILY OR COMBINATION SKIN The over-production of sebum creates oily skin, which has a shiny appearance. Hormonal changes during puberty or adulthood can increase the amount of oil produced. Blocked sebaceous glands can lead to enlarged pores, blackheads and spots.

Although oily skin is more resistant to the effects of ageing than dry skin, you must avoid using harsh cleansers and soaps which can strip the oil away leading to increased oil production and a dry, flaky surface. Gentle cleansers are required.

Take care to moisturise the eyes, neck and cheeks which are often dry and use a non-comedogenic (non-pore-blocking) moisturiser.

SENSITIVE SKIN Up to 80 per cent of women believe that they have sensitive skin, but dermatologists put the true figure between 15 and 20 per cent. Sensitive skin reacts to internal or external stimuli and the signs of sensitivity are redness or blotchiness, a feeling of heat or a burning, stinging sensation, swelling, bumps under the skin and flakiness. The skin reacts when it comes into contact with an allergen or an irritant. Allergens cause the immune system to react and further contact with the allergen will lead to more severe reactions. Avoid using soap, particularly on the face, as it can impair the functioning of the skin's acid mantle and leave it vulnerable to allergens and irritants. Try using hypo-allergenic skincare, suncare and cosmetic products which will have been screened of potentially irritating or allergic substances. You should also experiment with different brands of shampoo, conditioner, styling lotions and sprays.

Refer to the section Skin Problems Solved for further advice.

The skin is the largest organ of the body. It is divided into three main layers: the epidermis is the outermost layer and consists of dead and dying skin cells that are constantly being rubbed away by friction and replaced by new skin cells that are produced at the base of the epidermis. This process takes between 21 and 28 days. Cell turnover begins gradually slowing down after the age of about 25. The epidermis is the only layer that cosmetic preparations can penetrate. The dermis supports, nourishes and supplies the epidermis with nutrients. Sebaceous glands, sweat glands, collagen fibres, nerves and hair follicles are located in this layer. The sub-dermis consists of fat cells which act as a cushion under the dermis and epidermis providing a firm foundation and helping to preserve body heat.

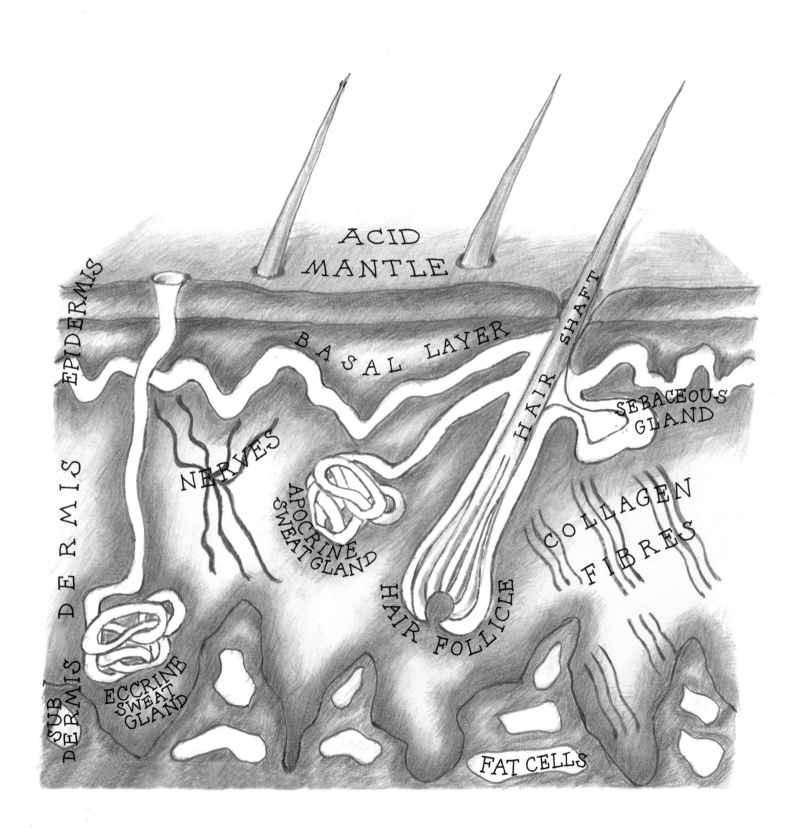

Two-thirds of women in the U.K.
believe that a quick splash with soap and water
is sufficient to clean their skin.

CLEANSING

While we may like the simplicity
of this process, most of us do not realise
that by using soap we are
drying our complexions, leaving
them susceptible to external aggressors.

Increasingly, it is being recognised that cleansing the skin is not just a perfunctory process.

Done correctly, it can have a beneficial effect on the skin. But done incorrectly, it can be positively detrimental.

So how do we get it right? First, ditch the soap and water when it comes to cleansing your face, and consider using a soap-free cleanser for your body, especially if you have very dry skin. Soap breaks down the skin's protective acid mantle, and although normal skin can repair this protective barrier in a matter of hours, it can take older or prematurely-aged skins more than 24 hours, leaving them vulnerable to dehydration and sensitivity in the meantime. It is also notoriously difficult to rinse soap away efficiently and alkaline deposits left behind can break down the skin's lipids (natural oils).

The much kinder option is to use a soap-free cleanser or cleansing lotion formulated for your particular skin's needs which will remove impurities and, if necessary, excess oil, while respecting your skin's natural balance. Today many cleansers also offer skin treatment, soothing and even anti skin-ageing benefits.

NORMAL SKIN can be cleansed with a soap-free, wash-off cleanser or a light, lotion cleanser plus a freshener. Gently massage cleanser into the face with your fingertips, and leave it on the face ideally for two to three minutes before removing so that the skin can benefit fully from the cleansing and treatment benefits.

DRY SKIN just loves cream cleansers. Soothing ingredients such as honeysuckle and calendula may be included to calm the skin and wheatgerm and soybean oil, for instance, will leave the skin supple. Remove with cotton wool pads and use an alcohol-free freshener to remove any last traces. Dampening the cotton wool slightly before adding the freshener will avoid wastage.

OILY OR COMBINATION SKIN can be cleansed with a soap-free or a wipe-off cleanser. Adequate cleansing is important for oily skins because excess oil can lead to enlarged pores. Moisturisers will be added to oily skin cleansers to ensure that your skin has a good 'after feel' and that moisture loss is prevented. Like cream cleansers, some soap-free cleansers are effective when left on the skin for two to three minutes before rinsing off. Cleansers that contain small amounts of the exfoliating agents 'alpha hydroxy acids' can be helpful in refining the texture of oily skin, but take care with these products if your skin is sensitive.

SENSITIVE SKIN should never be exposed to soap and water. Wipe-off or soap-free hypo-allergenic cleansers with soothing ingredients are the most suitable, and never use toners that contain alcohol.

EXFOLIATING You should exfoliate your skin once or twice a week, using either a facial exfoliator or an exfoliating mask to lift away the top layer of dead skin cells. However, if you are using skincare preparations that contain alpha hydroxy acids you won't need to use a manual exfoliator as well. With a facial scrub, you should never rub the skin until it becomes pink or stretch the skin. Check that the product you use contains no rough particles. Apply the exfoliator to damp skin, massage gently in, then rinse thoroughly. Avoid the eye area and don't use exfoliators on sensitive skins or skins that have severe acne, unless on a dermatologist's advice.

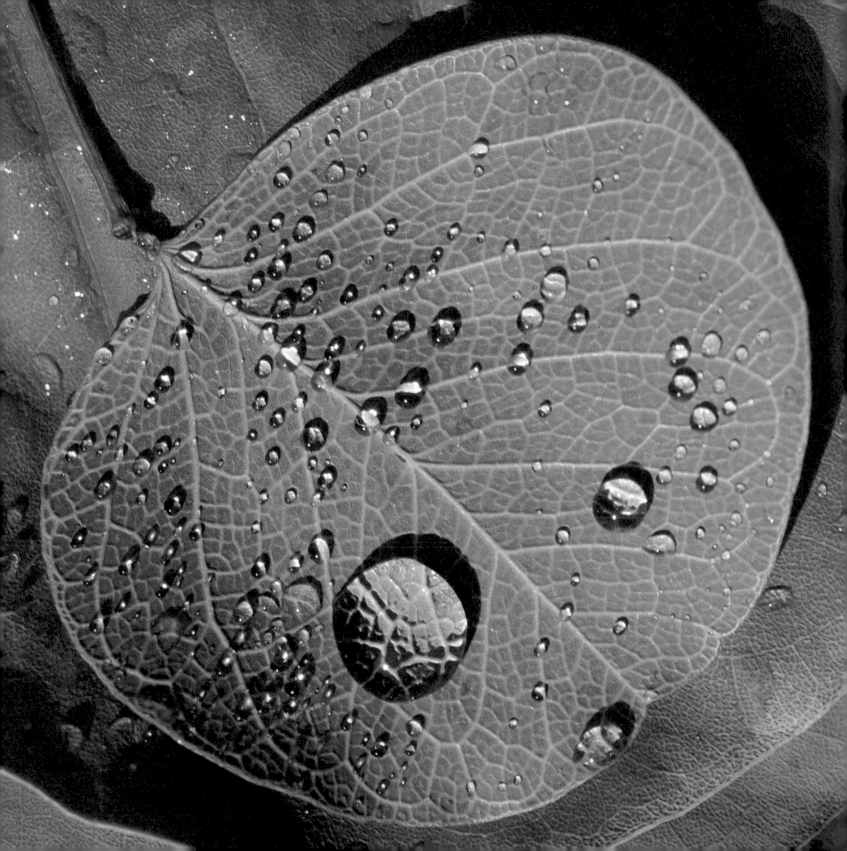

MOISTURISE

Moisturisers don't simply make your face and body feel soft. They are your skin's defence system against a hostile world, delivering water to your skin's outer layers and preventing moisture loss to your surroundings.

There's no question about it: dehydrated skin is more likely to develop lines and wrinkles than strong, supple skin. A well-moisturised complexion looks fresher and brighter, too, because the smoother surface reflects light more efficiently.

Every skin type needs a moisturiser, even oily skins. If you have an oily or combination complexion, use a product formulated for your skin type. It needs to be non-comedogenic, that is, it will not contain ingredients that could block the pores and so lead to spots.

Dry skins will drink up enriched formulations, although today even the lightest texture moisturisers can be super-hydrators thanks to high-tech moisturising ingredients. The texture of your moisturiser, therefore, can be a matter of personal taste. Maintaining the water content of a dry skin is especially important in order to prevent the condition from worsening.

You should seek advice if you find you develop persistant flaky, scaly patches, particularly around the nose. They may indicate an allergic reaction in which case any product, including a moisturiser, may irritate it further. Refer to the Skin Problems Solved section.

Modern moisturisers are packed with additional skin benefits. Protective sunscreens are often included, and ingredients reputed for their anti skin-ageing actions, pollution shielding complexes and desensitising factors are also frequently present.

Do you need a night cream, too? You certainly will if you have very dry or dry skin. In fact, many 'dream creams' are formulated as special treatments, designed to improve the skin's natural repair systems.

Eye contour creams and gels

Eye products perform a number of functions. They maintain optimum moisture levels in an area where the skin is super-fine and highly mobile. Moisturising the skin here will smooth out the skin, so that eyeshadows do not sit in any lines or grooves, and some eye contour creams will also offer some protection from ultraviolet rays. Ingredients may also be included that will help to reduce puffiness and dark shadows. You should avoid using your regular moisturiser in the eye area because it's texture could make the skin puffy and it may contain a fragrance that could irritate.

Neck creams

You will find plenty of people who will tell you that you don't need a special cream for the neck. Well, it depends on what you are using on your face already. The neck is an area that is very susceptible to showing the signs of ageing. It is a highly mobile area and loss of elasticity can lead to slack skin. It may also be drier than your face. A neck cream that has a firming action and that also contains UVA and UVB filters will both improve the appearance of the neck and help to prevent further damage being caused by the sun. It is well worth applying it morning and evening.

ANTI SKIN-AGEING STRATEGIES

Like it or not, we live in an age-conscious society and youthful-looking skin is intrinsically linked to current concepts of beauty. Attitudes are slowly changing, but lines and wrinkles are still seen as undesirable by the majority of women.

Advances in cosmetic and surgical techniques mean that skin firmness and tone, smoothness and resilience can all be improved. However, the potential drawbacks of any surgical method should be considered carefully first.

Prevention is the most important anti skin-ageing tactic you can adopt. Wearing a moisturiser each day will help to prevent moisture loss from the outer layers of the skin into the atmosphere, while providing a protective barrier against skin-sensitising elements such as pollution and smoke. Smoking is increasingly being highlighted as a major enemy of healthy skin, damaging fats in the top layers of the skin and increasing dryness, lines and wrinkles.

Sun filters are another key preventative weapon. Consider using a daily moisturiser that contains sunfilters, even in winter when ageing UVA rays are still present. Don't expose your skin to the sun or, if you do, be sure to wear a high factor (SPF15) sunscreen with 4 star UVA protection.

The Anti Skin-Ageing Challenge

It is possible to diminish the visible signs of ageing with at-home treatments. Cell regeneration can be encouraged and fine lines combatted by using **alpha hydroxy acid** preparations. Usually combined with moisturisers, these products contain one or more AHAs, such as lactic acid from milk, glycolic acid from sugar cane, citric acid from citrus fruit and malic acid from apples.

The AHAs sweep away dead skin cells and surface cells to help revitalise your skin, leaving behind a smoother, softer texture and clearer skin tone. Anti skin-ageing benefits will be seen within a month. Acne-prone complexions can also see improvements.

Research has shown that glycolic acid can also increase the water-binding properties of the outer layer of skin, the epidermis, delaying the drying-out effect that ageing has.

Different products contain different concentrations of AHAs. A slight tingling sensation may be noticed the first few times that you use a product and is quite normal. It does not mean that you are experiencing an allergic reaction. AHAs are increasingly being incorporated in hand, foot and body lotions, in shampoos to treat flaky scalps and in make-up to help smooth the skin in the long-term.

As well as containing AHAs, many moisturisers, treatment products and sunscreens now feature antioxidants. The most popular **antioxidants** are vitamins and vitamin derivatives, such as vitamin A, C and E or betacarotene. Some plant extracts are also increasingly used for their antioxidant properties.

Antioxidants work by helping to neutralise the effects of skin-damaging **'free radicals'** - highly reactive molecules that are triggered by a wide range of factors including ultraviolet light, ozone, pollution and smoking and which are partly responsible for the changes we see as ageing. Research into new forms of antioxidants is on-going.

Enzymes have also joined the anti skin-ageing arsenal. Naturally present in our bodies, enzymes are included in skincare products either to help improve certain skin functions or to block the action of other enzymes that play a role in skin ageing. Collagenase, for example, is the enzyme that destroys collagen and elastin.

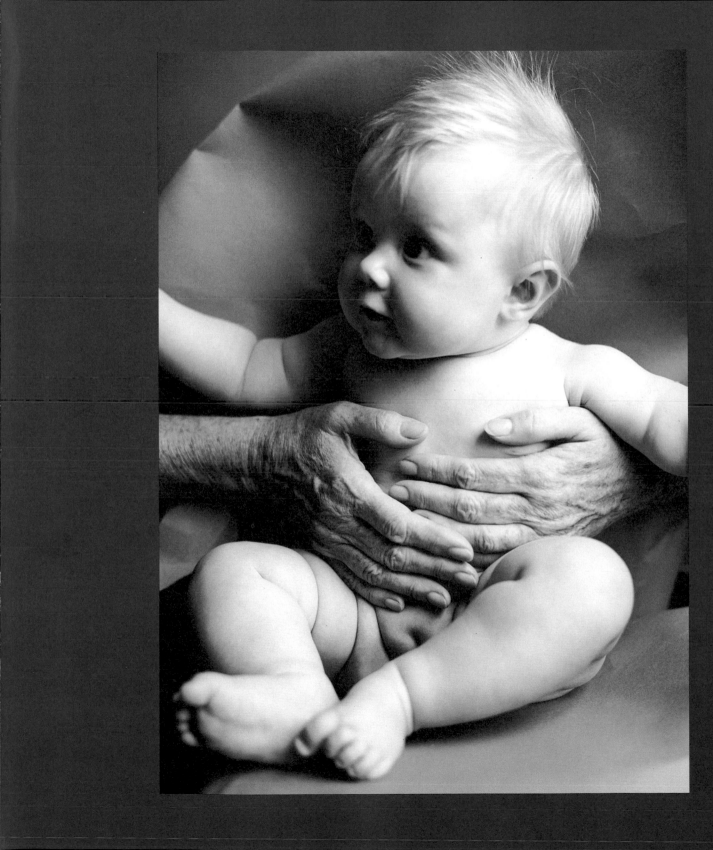

Fast Firmers

Loss of skin firmness is one of the most crucial aspects of skin ageing. When collagen and elastin become damaged, the skin sags and facial contours become less defined.

Skin firming complexes work in the outer layer of the skin to promote a healthier looking complexion by supplying lipids called ceramides to help strengthen the intercellular lipids. By improving the barrier function of the skin, they also help to prevent water loss.

Beauty salons offer a variety of treatments that claim to increase skin firmness. Often called 'non surgical face lifts', they use tiny electric currents to, they say, stimulate the skin's regenerative processes and tighten the muscles.

Photo-Ageing
Photo-ageing refers to skin damage caused by ultraviolet light, principally from exposure to sunlight or from using sunbeds. The skin's supportive network of collagen and elastin is undermined, leading to wrinkles. A variety of dermatologist-prescribed treatment creams have captured the attention of women in recent years because of their ability to repair sun-induced, premature ageing.

Collagen Injections
Collagen can be used to fill out the lips, which naturally become thinner over time, and to plump out vertical lines around the lips, nose to mouth lines, frown lines and forehead wrinkles. A sensitivity test must be performed beforehand. The body metabolises collagen, so treatments must be repeated around every three months and can prove expensive.

Laser Technology
A new form of skin 'peeling' is being carried out by Ultra-Pulse Laser. A high-energy light beam is emitted in millisecond bursts, so that the uppermost layer of the skin is not burned and there is claimed to be less bleeding, swelling and crusting than with other forms of surgical skin peeling.

Face Lifts
Currently it is not simply the skin that is lifted and tightened, but often the muscle is lifted as well to give a better result. Individual areas of the face can be operated on, such as the cheeks, jowls, forehead or neck. The safety of all cosmetic surgery is dependent on the skill of the operator. Skin peels can cause scarring and face lifts will not necessarily eliminate lip wrinkles, crow's feet or other irregularities in skin texture.

Hollywood stars in need of an instant face lift for the cameras used freshly whisked egg whites. Instead you can apply a few drops of a firming serum onto a moisturised skin.

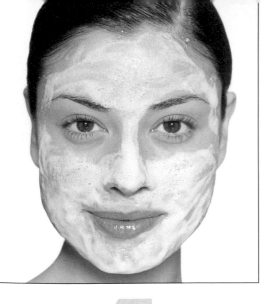

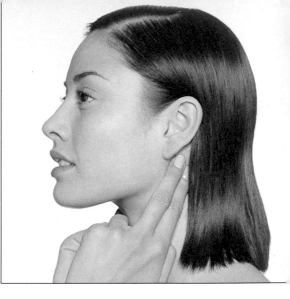

Massaging your skin will increase micro-circulation, bringing nutrients to the cells, helping to release tension and improve lymphatic drainage. The lymph system drains excess fluid from the cells, reducing puffiness. To help stimulate the lymph, circle behind the ears using the fingertips of each hand for a minute. Now press down the neck and circle on the breastbone, just above your breasts.

1

Cleanse your face thoroughly and remove any eye make-up.
Wet your face with warm water and very gently massage on a facial exfoliator suited to your skin type. Remember not to pull or scrub at the skin, or to rub until the skin changes colour.

3

Apply a replenishing serum to the skin, or an aromatherapy oil that is ready-diluted for facial massage. Using the first and second fingers of each hand, rhythmically stroke your forehead using light, upward movements, one hand following the other. Start at the centre of the forehead and move out to one side, work your way slowly across to the other side and then back to the centre.

Is your skin in need of a quick lift? You can recreate the beauty salon facial in your own home, and at a fraction of the price. The following 15 minute routine is the perfect reviver before a party, or simply for those times when your complexion is looking less than perky.

Place your hands along the sides of your nose and gently press and sweep out towards the hairline. Repeat six times, moving down the face as you do so. When you reach the chin, use the thumbs and first fingers to pinch the skin as you move along the jawbone, from the centre of the chin out to the sides.

Starting at the centre of your face, gently pinch along the length of each eyebrow. Repeat several times.

Finish by closing your eyes and placing the pads of your first two fingers at the temples. Circle slowly six times. Press into your temples, hold for five seconds and repeat.

Apply a face mask chosen for your skin's needs. Some masks, such as self-heating 'sauna' masks, are designed to help purify the skin and unblock pores. Others contain hydrating and firming ingredients to give a lift to fatigued complexions. Remove the mask and apply a refreshing eye gel and a moisturiser, smoothing it on from the chest upwards.

SKIN SOLUTIONS

Q I have developed very dry patches of skin and my regular body lotion does not appear to make a difference. Can you help?

A You may have a form of dermatitis known as eczema. It is estimated that one in ten people suffer from eczema at some point in their lives. Dry skin is one of the key features of eczema and emollients, which form a protective barrier to seal moisture into the skin, are a main feature in its treatment. You should consult your G.P. for a precise diagnosis.

The main types of dermatitis are:

Atopic: This form is an allergic reaction and often appears in the first year of life. It is thought to run in families and is part of a group of atopic conditions which include eczema, asthma and hay fever. The main symptom is overall dryness, usually accompanied by overwhelming itchiness. The skin may become inflamed and crack and split.

Seborrhoeic: There are two types of seborrhoeic dermatitis. One is most common in babies and the other in young adults. Oily parts of the body such as the scalp, face, groin and chest are generally affected and it is not normally itchy.

Contact: There are also two types of contact dermatitis: irritant and allergic. The irritant form is caused by exposure to agents such as soaps, detergents, industrial chemicals, hair dyes and bleaches. Allergic contact dermatitis is caused by specific sensitivity to materials like nickel, chrome or rubber.

Varicose: This form of dermatitis is found in elderly people and people with varicose veins.

Discoid: Usually confined to the arms and legs, scaly, itchy, coin-shaped patches that can blister and weep.

Q There are dark brown patches on my temples and around my lips. Can they be treated?

A These are probably **pigmentation marks** - dark areas of the skin's protective melanin which have been triggered by the sun, the contraceptive pill or pregnancy. Fade creams are available which will help to lighten them, but they take six weeks or more to have an effect. You should then wear a sunscreen with an SPF of 15 or more when sunbathing to help prevent them recurring. If a mole changes in shape or colour, you should consult your G.P. without delay as it could indicate skin cancer.

Skin problems are more common than you would imagine. The best plan of action is to seek expert advice.

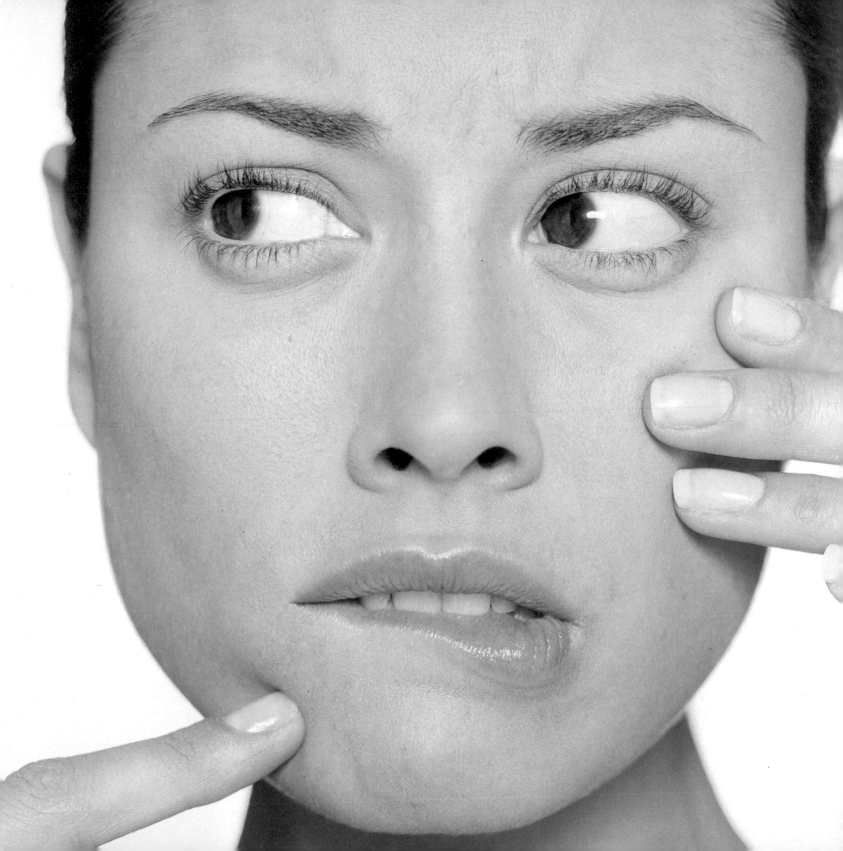

MORE SOLUTIONS

Q I have heard that chocolate does not cause **spots**. Is this true?

A Yes, it is. No link has ever been established between **acne** (the generic name for spots) and any type of food. Acne is an inflammatory disorder where the skin reacts abnormally to the hormone testosterone, affecting the production of sebum, (the skin's natural lubricating oil). In addition, skin cells in the hair follicles become sticky and dead cells accumulate there, blocking the flow of sebum. Bacteria then multiply in the stagnant oil. Stress may be implicated, because it triggers the excess production of testosterone.

You should use a gentle, medicated cleanser and spot treatment products. Harsh products will dry and irritate the skin. Avoid soap and water. Moisturisers should be **non-comedogenic** (non-pore blocking).

Exposure to the sun will exacerbate the condition. Some drugs and contraceptive pills can aggravate or bring on acne.

If your acne is severe, or if you do not see an improvement in your skin within two months of using over-the-counter products, ask your GP to refer you to a specialist, who will be aware of the very latest treatments. Dermatologists report that most people do not seek help soon enough and that today, nobody should be left scarred by acne.

Spots can be squeezed, but only with great care. If you see blood, you have squeezed too much. If you squeeze too hard, you will push the infection deeper into the tissues and may cause scarring. Therefore, avoid squeezing if possible.

'Whiteheads' or milia are small, keratin cysts which are not related to acne but to genetics. They can be pricked out with a sterile pin by a beauty therapist.

Q I have developed very red cheeks and I look as though I am constantly **blushing**. What should I do?

A Recurrent blushing attacks and permanently red skin with broken veins or acne-like lumps, are indications of a skin condition called **rosacea**. A disorder of the skin and blood vessels of the face, it most commonly occurs in women between the ages of 25 and 50. Because it tends to run in families, many believe that their florid or rosy complexion is simply a family characteristic. However, without treatment, rosacea (pronounced row-say-sha) steadily worsens and can become severe. It is important, therefore, to report symptoms to your GP, rather than simply putting them down to age, food or an allergy.

A facial gel which contains an **antibiotic** has been found to be as effective as oral antibiotics. Green-tinted colour corrective moisturisers and concealers are available to help conceal the redness and broken veins.

SUN

When it comes to tanning,
we face a dilemma. Are you willing to
accept the prospect of lines and
wrinkles, age spots, broken veins and
potentially, skin cancer as a trade off for
a so-called healthy, golden glow?
If you are going to tan, recognising
when your skin is most at risk is vital.

THE INTELLIGENT

WOMAN'S TAN

It is important to know your individual skin tanning type in order to understand how vulnerable your skin is to the sun and so that you can estimate how long a Sun Protection Factor (SPF) can protect your skin from burning. The maximum unprotected times given are approximate, relate to UK sun and will vary according to location and local conditions.

FAIR OR RED HAIR, PALE SKIN AND FRECKLES AND CHILDREN

Reaction to the sun: Your skin cannot tan

Maximum time you can sunbathe unprotected without burning:
10 minutes

FAIR HAIR, BLUE EYES, MID TO PALE SKIN TONES

Reaction to the sun: You tan minimally and burn easily

Maximum time you can sunbathe unprotected without burning:
10 - 15 minutes

DARK HAIR AND EYES, MID TO PALE SKIN TONE

Reaction to the sun: You tan gradually, but have a tendency to burn

Maximum time you can sunbathe unprotected without burning:
20 minutes

DARK HAIR AND EYES, OLIVE OR DARK SKIN TONE

You tan easily and rarely burn

Maximum time you can sunbathe unprotected without burning:
20 minutes or more, depending on how dark your natural skin tone is.

Choosing the best sun protection for your skin can be a very confusing business. Here's how to get it right.

It is vital to know your personal tanning type. In addition, you need to take into account where in the world you will be and at what time of the year. Bear in mind that the sun at its most powerful between 11 am and 3 pm and remember that the nearer to the equator you are, the stronger the sun is at all times.

WHICH SPF?

Dermatologists have a straightforward answer: wear a sunscreen with an SPF, (or Sun Protection Factor), of 15 at all times to protect yourself from the burning UVB rays, and check that it offers good UVA protection, too.

An SPF indicates how long you can sunbathe for without burning. So, if your skin type permits 10 minutes of sunbathing when you are not protected, a cream with an SPF of 15 gives you 15 times × 10 minutes, that is, 150 minutes before your skin will start to burn.

WHAT ARE UVA RAYS?

UVA rays are weaker than the burning UVBs, but travel deeper into the living dermis of the skin. The protection offered against UVA rays is usually indicated by the Star System. On the back of a pack which uses the system you will find up to four stars, which is the best level of UVA protection currently available.

EXTRA CARE

Babies under 6 months should not be exposed to the sun at all. Toddlers and young children should be covered up as much as possible with long, loose clothes with a close weave and should wear a broad-brimmed hat and sunglasses, in addition to being protected with a high factor sunscreen, especially on exposed skin. Remember that the protective capacity of clothing is greatly reduced when it is wet.

Did you know that you should apply sunscreen 15 minutes before you go outside, in order to allow it to penetrate the stratum corneum (the outer layer of the skin)? Slop it on thickly before you get into your swimsuit or you risk missing some very vulnerable areas of skin around the line of your costume. Re-apply it frequently unless it is sweatproof or waterproof.

We tend
to burn
when we
least
expect
to and
local
conditions
can
significantly
increase
the
risk of
burning.

YOU SHOULD TAKE EXTRA CARE IN THE FOLLOWING CIRCUMSTANCES:
When it is windy, there is a **cool breeze** or it is overcast. We tend to be lulled into a false sense of security if we cannot feel the heat of the sun on our skin and forget that the burning ultraviolet rays are present even when it is **overcast**. The heat that we feel on our skin comes from infra-red rays, which probably play a part in skin damage, not the ultra-violet rays which do the most damage.

If you are on a mountain - beware. The higher you climb, the higher the chances of frying yourself. UV intensity increases with **altitude**.

When sunbathing with a friend or partner. The tendency may be to use the same SPF sunscreen - but you could be very different **tanning types**.

When you are walking, **gardening** or playing a sport. Sixty per cent of people forget to apply a sunscreen for outdoor pursuits. Schools are increasingly recognising the importance of protecting children while they are playing games or are in the **playground**. When you are swimming, UV rays can penetrate several metres of water. If you are swimming or in water for over 20 minutes your skin is more likely to burn, leaving you looking like a lobster.

When **sailing**, windsurfing, floating peacefully on a lilo or sunning yourself in a whitewashed suntrap. Any **reflective** surface, including sand, will dramatically increase your exposure. You can also burn in the shade.

SKIN CANCER
There are three main types of skin cancer. **Basal cell** and **squamous cell carcinoma** tend to occur in older people. Over 95 per cent of these types of skin cancer are curable. **Malignant melanoma** (MM) is very different to the other two forms of skin cancer and, if undetected, can spread to other parts of the body and be fatal. It occurs in young adults as well as in older people and is the third most common cancer in women aged between 15 and 34. However, if it is treated early there is a very good chance that it can be cured.

In women, the most common place for MM to develop is on the calf of the leg. In men it is on the trunk, and particularly on the back. Most melanomas start on a pigmented patch, such as an unusual freckle or a new or existing blackish-brownish mole. They grow and change shape or colour, and later signs may be a **spot**, **freckle** or **mole** which is itchy, tender, bleeds or has a crust. If you suspect a melanoma, see your doctor immediately.

HOT STUFF

If you get sunburned, you need lots of rehydrating ('isotonic') drinks to replace the salts you will have sweated out. You should also cool your overheated system by soaking in a tepid bath. Apply a gel formulated to soothe sunburnt skin - aloe vera is effective - or calamine lotion. Milk or natural yoghurt will help if you don't have anything else available. Avoid using oils, which may seal heat into the skin, and do not expose your skin to the sun at all until the reaction has subsided. If the burn is severe or the skin is broken, you should seek medical help.

Prickly heat An itchy rash that can be red, scaly, lumpy or blistered, is probably what dermatologists call polymorphic light eruption, or PLE. It is mainly triggered by UVA rays, so a four star UVA, high factor sunscreen is recommended if you know you may be susceptible.

White patches After a holiday, you may notice you have white, untanned areas of skin where you were not covered up. These may be the result of a common yeast that is present on everyone's skin undergoing a change which then affects pigmentation. Known as **pityriasis versicolor**, it is usually easily treated using a special shampoo, applied neat to the skin and left on. Treatment takes about six weeks and it may be some time after that before the skin recovers and starts to produce pigment again. Contrary to popular belief, pityriasis versicolor is not caught from sunbeds. The condition is sometimes confused with vitiligo, which is an immune response and much more difficult to treat.

Skin repair Are you concerned that you overdid the sunbathing before you knew how damaging the sun could be? Well, you can help your skin to repair some of the damage. There is new evidence to show that by wearing a high factor sunscreen or moisturiser with an SPF of 15 and good UVA protection throughout the year, you will help repair mechanisms in your skin to kick into action. You may be able to repair 30 per cent of the damage. Daily protection is important because ageing UVA rays surround us constantly and can pass through glass.

Antioxidants such as vitamins A, C and E can help to neutralise the highly reactive free radicals which are generated by UV light and which cause cell damage. They are increasingly being included in suncreens and after-sun lotion, so check to see if they are present before you buy.

Sunglasses

Ok, we know that sunglasses are seen by most of us as a style accessory. The attitude is, if they look good then that's good enough. Your eyes, however, do need protection. Both UVA and UVB rays can contribute to impaired vision and even blindness. Blue light can damage the retina. Sunglasses that carry the British Standard BS2724 will significantly reduce UV rays and blue light.

In Australia, there is a campaign to encourage people to choose wrap-around styles.

Nowadays it's so easy to get a bronzed body or sun-kissed face from a tube that sweating away under an unforgiving sun or, worse still, on a sunbed, is not only undesirable, but unnecessary. You'd be amazed at how many women today fake their tans.

Choose from instant bronzers and skin tints that last until you wash them off, self-tans with skin tints to give immediate, cosmetic colour until a longer-lasting hue develops and self-tans that develop in two to four hours and last for four days.

INSTANT SUNSHINE

The colour boosters listed below wash off or can be removed with cleanser.

Tinted Moisturiser: Apply with your fingertips, avoiding your brows and hairline. Look for formulations with light diffusing particles and protective sun filters.

Bronzing Powders and Complexion Pearls: Build up the colour gradually. These are best dusted onto the areas that would naturally catch the sun first - cheekbones, chin, nose and forehead.

Complexion or Bronzing Gel: Apply using fingertips, particularly to the same areas as a bronzing powder.

Skin Tint: Applied with a damp cosmetic sponge, this is a brown-tinted lotion or cream which is formulated for either the face or the body. Allow the product to dry thoroughly before dressing.

Stocking Cream: As you would guess, this can be applied to the legs to give a very smooth, tanned appearance. Good for concealing small veins. Apply with a cosmetic sponge or your hands and allow to dry before dressing.

LONGER-LASTING COLOUR

The active ingredient contained in fake tans is DHA (Dihydroxyacetone), which interacts naturally with the proteins found in your skin's upper layer. Because the colour developed by DHA is dependent on the amount of protein found in the upper layer of the skin, it is best to use a product that is formulated to give a light self-tan on the first application. You can re-apply the product to achieve a deeper colour.

The 'tan' only lasts up to four days because as the skin's surface layer is renewed, the tan disappears. Facial skin cells have a particularly fast turnover so you may need to top-up your fake tan more frequently than every few days.

Whether you are applying to the face or the body, start

by using a gentle exfoliating scrub followed by a moisturiser to avoid the product grabbing onto drier patches. Apply to the face using tiny, circular motions. Avoid your eyebrows and hairline as colour may collect there: a smudge of petroleum jelly will protect them if necessary. Avoid the palms of the hands and the soles of the feet as these areas do not tan naturally. Wash your hands as soon as you have finished.

Allow 2-4 hours after applying before bathing or swimming to ensure that you don't wash away any of the DHA, creating an uneven finish.

For the body, you may well find that spray-on self-tans are the quickest and easiest to use.

If you envisage a carrot when you see the words "fake tan", don't worry. New formulations mean that streaky, bright orange legs have more or less been relegated to recent history. Should you find that a self-tanning lotion does look obvious, fade away creams are available which work in minutes to reduce the colour.

YOUR MAKE-UP

The key to a great-looking make-up lies in knowing which products to use for the look, and the best way to apply them.

FOUNDATIONS

Gone are the days when a foundation would sit mask-like on the face. Today's bases are more like a second skin, created to help you look just like you, only naturally better.

Modern make-up is very much a treatment proposition. Foundations shield your skin from the elements with ultraviolet filters and anti-pollution complexes, moisturising factors to improve the condition of dry skins, while oil-controlling agents help to rebalance greasy skins. Anti skin-ageing ingredients like alpha hydroxy acids even reduce the appearance of fine lines.

There are two other essential aspects to finding the right foundation for your skin: texture and colour.

TEXTURE TALK

A foundation should suit your skin type and the conditions under which it will be worn. Whereas a sheer, barely-there hint of cover may well be right for the daytime, an evening in the steamy atmosphere of a nightclub calls for a base that is lasting and smear-proof.

Make-up base: A transparent emulsion that is applied to the face before foundation to keep your skin shine-free and your foundation looking fresh for longer. Apply moisturiser first to areas that need it.

Light diffusing: Specially coated pigments in these foundations bounce light off the skin's surface, giving a more radiant and youthful appearance.

Tinted moisturiser: Suits all skin types, except very oily skins with open pores. Often available in a choice of shades.

Mousse: Very light, see-through base for all skin types. Especially good for young and oily skins.

Liquid: Usually water-based, these give lightweight coverage. Check the label to find the formulation that is suited to your skin: For instance, 'Matte' or 'oil-free' are good for oily skins; 'dewy' or 'moisturising' are better for drier skins.

Creme: Usually offering medium to maximum coverage, these are most suitable for dry skins.

Compact: Time-saving formulations combining foundation and powder, applied with a latex sponge. Good for all skin types and ideal for making up on the run. Oily and combination complexions may need a little extra loose powder applied to the T-zone.

Treatment: Many foundations now bring with them a range of skin treatment benefits. Anti skin-ageing vitamins, firming complexes, and high-powered moisturising or oil-controlling ingredients are just some of the technological advantages a foundation can offer your complexion.

COLOUR MATCHES

Two things are essential when shopping for foundation: a clean face and a hand mirror. It's no good thinking that you can get away with testing a product on the back of your hand - the skin here is a different shade and texture to facial skin.

When you have picked a foundation that suits your skin type, and which will give the coverage you feel comfortable with, check the colour by applying a small amount of the tester to the skin at the jawline. Wait at least five minutes for the product to adapt to the acidity levels in your skin and then go outside and inspect the colour with your mirror. You need to do this because artificial store lighting can alter the tone of a shade. If it looks natural in harsh daylight, you should consider buying it.

The right foundation will 'disappear' when applied to your skin, while smoothing out uneven tones in your complexion.

The latest thinking on foundation suggests that it should only be applied to the areas that need it. You can use it around the nose, chin and eye areas, for instance, and simply powder the rest of your face. Some make-up artists recommend applying liquid foundation with a very slightly damp sponge - squeezed out in a towel first - while others find that the warmth of the fingers gives a more blended result.

CONCEALERS

Make-up helps to hide imperfections we'd rather the rest of the world didn't see. Concealers, colour correctors and powders can be the make-up wearer's secret weapons.

Concealers Lack of sleep, illness and hereditary factors can all contribute to dark circles under the eyes. This is where a good concealer comes into its own. Light-reflective and moisturising properties give them the same benefits as your foundation.

Stick concealers are applied by make-up artists using a small, stiff brush - applying them straight from the stick can give too obvious a finish. Some can be quite greasy, and they are generally thicker in consistency than cream or liquid concealers, which are easier to apply on dark shadows and on the tiny purpley veins above the eye.

For the best results, apply concealer on top of your foundation - putting it on first can make it 'move' when you apply your base.

Colour Correctors come in liquid, stick or powder form and depending on your requirements, can brighten, add warmth or cool down your complexion. The rule of 'less is more' has never been more true than when you are applying colour correctors. You need just enough to cancel out the colour you are trying to correct. Seek the advice of a make-up consultant and if you are still unsure about how much to use, give them a miss altogether. They should be applied to problem areas only, rarely to the whole face.

A small amount mixed with your foundation or concealer will give the most natural effect. Green tones down rosy or highly-coloured skin; lilac or pink brighten; and yellow or peach will liven up a dull or pallid complexion.

Powders No woman wants to look as though she has just emerged from a bag of flour. Micro-fine powders are the answer: they go on like a dream and adhere to the skin, creating a smooth and silky finish. Look for a powder that is talc-free for a super-fine result, and that has sunscreens and moisturisers for added protection from the elements.

Loose powder is the powder to use to set foundation and beat shine, or use it on its own to improve the look of the skin while keeping it super-natural. Apply it with a velour puff, pressing well into the skin with a rocking motion - don't drag it over the skin or it will remove your base. Sweep away any excess with a large, soft, dome-shaped brush.

Pressed powder is portable, convenient and designed to mop up any unwanted shine that may appear during the day. Blotting your face with a tissue to eliminate excess oil before powdering will help to avoid a caked look caused by powder collecting on greasy patches.

Translucent powders are invisible and can be worn on any skin tone. Alternatively, sunny, yellow-based powders can improve the appearance of many skins and still look natural. Most women should avoid pink-based powders.

BLUSHER

Get the shade and the application right and blusher can be your best friend. Blushers now bring to your skin a wide array of treatment benefits. There are light diffusing particles to create a soft focus effect and make blusher easy to wear; silk powders and fine oils to moisturise the skin; and vitamin E and ultra-violet filters for their anti skin-ageing properties.

Tawny colours are flattering to most skins, while sandy pinks are good for giving a lift to fair skins. Deeper rose and plum shades are suitable for darker skins or for evening wear. The correct blusher colour will make you look healthy, while you will know if you are wearing the wrong shade as it will drain your skin of colour. It is vital that your blusher and lipstick colours work perfectly together.

There are boxes of powder pearls available, which cleverly combine three complementary colours that are guaranteed to work well for all skin tones.

Powder blusher usually looks its best when it is applied on top of foundation or powder. There are two chief ways to wear blusher - flushed-face and natural or chic and sophisticated.

Flush-faced Blush

The idea here is to look as though you have just had a great workout. Using a large blusher brush (this is essential), swirl the brush in the pot of powder pearls or blusher compact and blow off any excess powder. Smile and you will see the apple of your cheek. Now use a circular motion to apply the blusher to the apple only, building up the colour intensity very gradually if you feel the need.

Sophisticated Blush

This method will define your cheekbones, but application is more difficult if you don't have cheekbones to begin with. Using a smaller blusher brush, sweep it across the compact or the powder pearls and blow away any excess. Starting at a point directly below the centre of your eye, just below the middle of the cheek, apply the blusher underneath and onto the cheekbone, extending it into a subtle triangle shape as you move towards (but not into) the hairline. Dust the remaining powder along the temples. You can now add a paler colour right on top and above the cheekbone to highlight it further, if you wish. Be sure to check that the colour does not form "stripes" along your cheekbones.

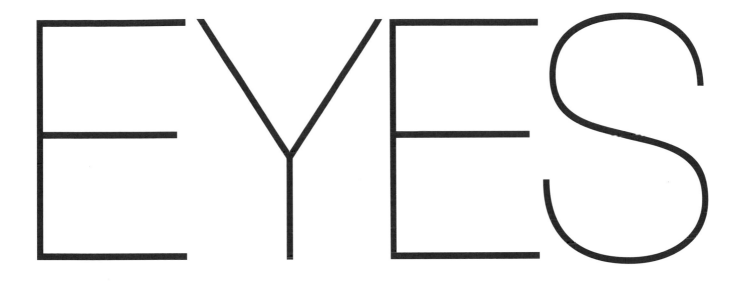

EYES

Neutral and natural, dark and smokey or shimmering and sparkling, your eyes can be shaped and shaded in an exciting variety of ways. Bring out the natural beauty of your eyes with these straightforward shading and colouring techniques.

E Y E
S H A P E R S

Eyeliners and shadows can do two things for your eyes: specific hues will intensify the colour of your eyes, while shading and highlighting techniques can create optical illusions to emphasise or refine the shape.

Eyeliner is the most difficult eye definer to apply. It requires an adept and steady hand and tends to dry very quickly. Balance your elbow in the palm of the opposite hand and rest your hand against your cheek when drawing the line. Start from the inner corner and work out. Eye pens, which are like felt pens, are usually easier to handle than brushes.

Eye pencils are much easier to use. The line should be smudged softly after application (rubber smudgers are supplied at the end of some pencils).

Eyeshadows should be as soft as velvet, crease-resistant and contain moisturisers and silk powders to improve the condition of the skin. Today many also contain sunscreens and vitamin E. A trace of pearlessence in a powder is a good thing as very matte eyeshadows can be ageing and look dull on the skin.

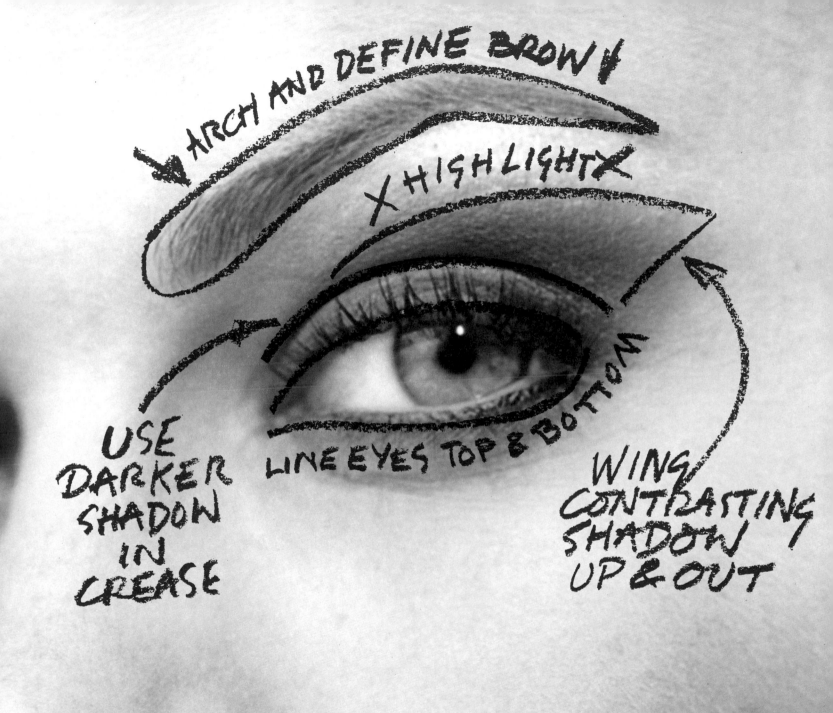

Eyebrows

Eyebrow shapes seem to change as fast as fashion itself. What remains constant is that they should be well-shaped and carefully defined. Look at a photograph of a model and you will see that the make-up artist has usually taken time over colouring and brushing them. When plucking, do so only from below the browline - you may find that this instantly opens up the eyes. To find out where your brows should finish, place a pencil at an angle from the bottom of your nose to the outer corner of your eye.

A clear brow gel is an easy way to give your eyebrows a little extra impact and to tame any wayward hairs.

Where possible, match your brows to your hair colour. Some women have their brows lightened or tinted. Use an eyebrow pencil to fill in any gaps, using just the lightest of feathery strokes. Very firm eyeshadow or a special eyebrow powder can be used, but sparingly or it may look too obvious.

Mascara

Curling the lashes immediately opens up the eyes. Don't press too hard - you don't want a kink mid-way along their length. Some make-up artists point out that if you apply mascara without curling the lashes first, you effectively close up the eye because you are making the lashes thicker and reducing the distance between the top and bottom rows.

Clear mascaras suit a natural look, thickening and defining without adding colour.

Experiment with where you apply mascara. Using it for all the top lashes (remembering to take it right into the inner corner), and just at the outer corner of the lower lashes may look more striking than wearing mascara along the whole length of the bottom row.

The applicator design is crucial to the finished effect. A "Christmas tree" type brush will give super-thick and separated lashes. A stick-type wand will give colour and direction. You should apply two coats, taking the brush as close to the roots as possible, and use an eyelash comb to separate any lashes that have stuck together after each coat.

Use a fibre-free mascara if you wear contact lenses or have sensitive eyes. Apply mascara after your contact lenses are in place.

Mascaras contain moisturisers to help keep the lashes soft and supple. Special films bond the colour to the lashes to prevent smudging. It is worth taking time to try colour variations in very black or nearly black, for instance.

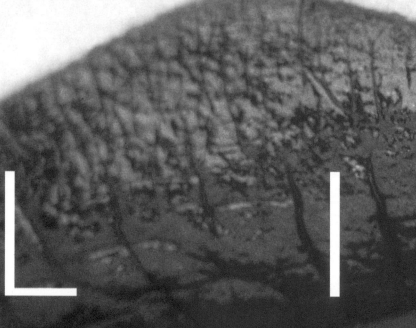

L I

The mouth is one of the most expressive parts of the body and for thousands of years women have painted their lips to make themselves visually more exciting.

P S

These days, we lavish our mouths
with lipstick not so much to attract a
partner, as to assert ourselves, bring
a flash of colour to our faces or to
complement our clothes.

Do you wear your lipstick down to a sharp, angled point? Transatlantic research says that you are extrovert, argumentative and perhaps even keen on hogging the limelight!

ALL CHANGE

If you're unhappy with the shape of your own mouth, you can correct it. Be warned though, a lip line which is obviously false runs the risk of looking clownlike, so alterations must be very subtle. Begin by applying a little foundation around the lip line to help camouflage it.

When someone is wearing pillarbox red on their lips, they are seen by others as confident, original and sure of their sexuality.

THIN LIPS

Rest your hand against your chin, and using a lip pencil, draw a line just outside your natural lip line. Most women find it easier to work from the outside of the mouth towards the middle. Then fill in with colour. Pale lip shades give the impression of a larger mouth. Liptip: Finish with a little gloss or highlighter on the upper lip; this adds fullness.

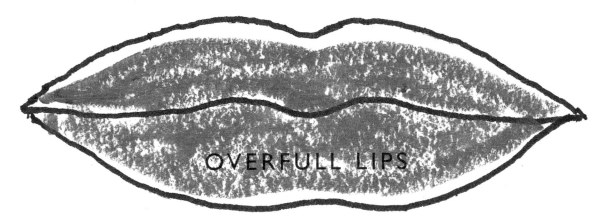

OVERFULL LIPS

After applying foundation over the whole of your lips, draw a line just inside your natural shape. Choose dark and mid-tone shades which will make the mouth recede, and avoid pale or shimmery shades which will do the opposite.

SHAPELESS LIPS

Apply foundation and powder first, and follow by outlining your desired shape. You can make an immediate difference to the appearance of your mouth by creating a 'cupid's bow', emphasising the 'm' in the centre of the top lip. Add fullness to the lower lip by drawing a line just outside the natural line.

SPECIAL EFFECTS

The type of lipstick you choose can change your overall look in seconds. This is how.

Moisturising, soothing, sheer or matte, lipsticks and glosses have a wide range of protective and beauty-enhancing properties.

Protective complexes are an important element in modern lipcolours. Vitamin E is included in good formulations because it has anti-ageing properties, and some lipcolours have sunscreens, which are very important if you are spending time outside - lips contain none of the skin's protective pigment.

Lasting lipcolours include a dye called eosin. The more eosin a lipstick contains, the longer it will last. There is a trade-off, however, in that eosin is an ingredient which is drying to the lips (it can also stain them slightly) so moisturisers are added to counteract this and to give a lasting lipstick a creamy texture. Eosin-free lipcolours are available if you have very dry lips.

Glosses/glazes These can be clear to provide gloss and shine when worn alone or over lipstick, or tinted and worn alone.

Transparent lip sheers Good for the summer, sheers give a wash of colour. Liptip: Make your own by mixing lipstick with a little vaseline in your palm and dabbing it onto the lips.

Semi-Matte and Matte Lipsticks which are longer-lasting. They look best when applied with the precision of a lip brush.

Pearl The shimmering texture of pearlised lipcolours is eye-catching and can help the lips to appear fuller.

Powder Highly-pigmented, powdery formulations which are usually quite dry in texture but long-lasting.

LIP SERVICE

From plumpers to primers, the myriad of optional lip extras will bring a smile to any lipstick lover's face.

Lip scuffs are for dry and flaky lips. They exfoliate the lips' top layer of skin to give a smoother, softer surface on which to apply your lipstick. Liptip: An effective do-it-yourself method is to use a soft-bristled toothbrush to brush a little lip balm onto the lips.

Lip primers smooth and moisturise your lips for the application of lipstick. Again, a good lipbalm will do the job sufficiently if your make-up budget is tight.

Lip plumpers are relatively new products that aim to give the impression of a full, sensuous, Bardot pout. Resembling a thick foundation, they work by seeping into the lips' tiny lines, plumping them out and thickening the surface layer to create a smooth base beneath your lipstick. They also contain molecules that attract moisture to slightly swell your lips.

Lip pencils should be firm-textured and closely match your lipstick. Alternatively, fill in the lips with pencil and apply gloss over the top.

A lip fix, or overcoat, is applied on top of your lipstick, where it forms a protective film and seals in the colour, preventing it from bleeding and feathering as well as extending wear. However, because of it's alcohol content, this type of product can be drying and should be used sparingly in winter and on chapped, flaky lips.

THE EVERLASTING KISS

With the right kind of lipstick and some careful application, you really can make sure your lipstick stays on your mouth and not every cup, glass or cheek you come into contact with. This method may seem time-consuming, but it is useful when you want to wear a bright colour for a whole evening.

First, prepare your lips with moisturiser, lip balm or a lip primer. The smoother the surface, the better your lipstick will look. It will also last longer and wear away evenly.

If you are planning to wear foundation, carry it over your lips to create a base for your lipstick to adhere to. Then lightly powder the area with loose or pressed powder and sweep away any excess with a large brush.

Most people need to line their lips to create a defined edge as well as to prevent lipstick - especially bright colours - from feathering. The lips can be filled with lipliner, as well. Unless you want an obvious outline to your mouth, don't use a liner that is more than a shade darker than your lipstick.

A lip brush allows you to build up colour for a lasting, professional-looking finish. Load the brush with colour and follow your natural lip contour carefully, working inwards from the outer corners of your mouth. Use your other hand to steady your working elbow to ensure accuracy.

Then take a tissue, pull it apart and press one layer to your mouth. Hold it in place and dust some loose powder over the tissue, which will act like a sieve, helping to set the colour. Dabbing a tiny bit of powder around the line of the mouth with your finger will help to prevent the edges from smudging.

Apply a second coat of lipstick with your brush and use the other layer of tissue to repeat the blotting process.

Liptip: Place your index finger halfway into your mouth with your lips closed around it and pull it slowly out. Any excess lipstick will come away on your finger, and not your teeth.

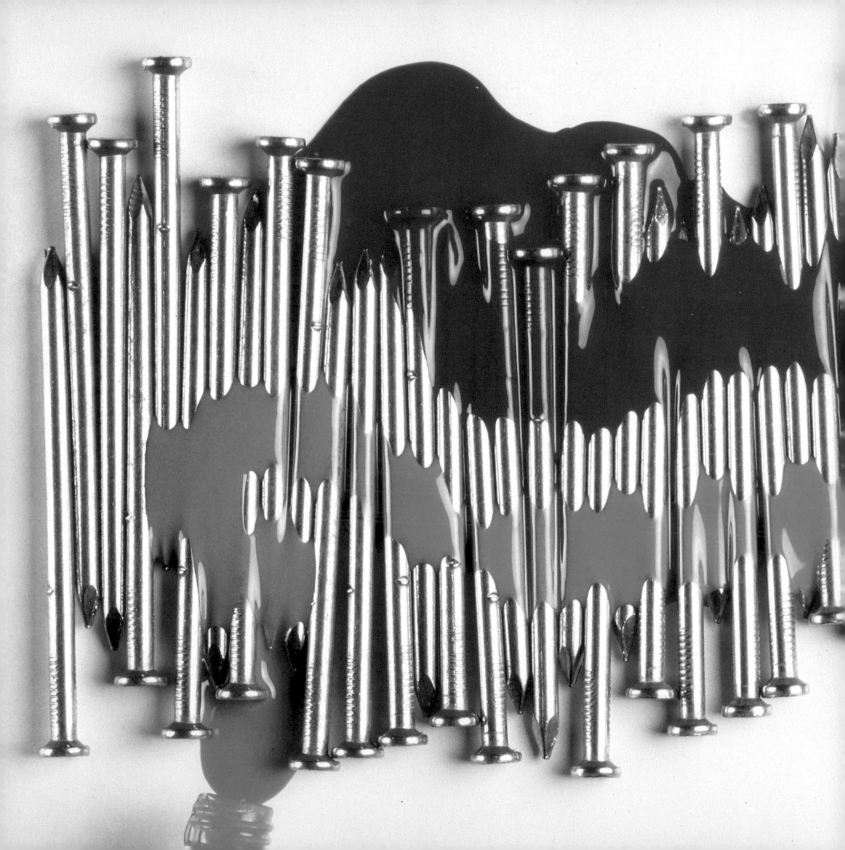

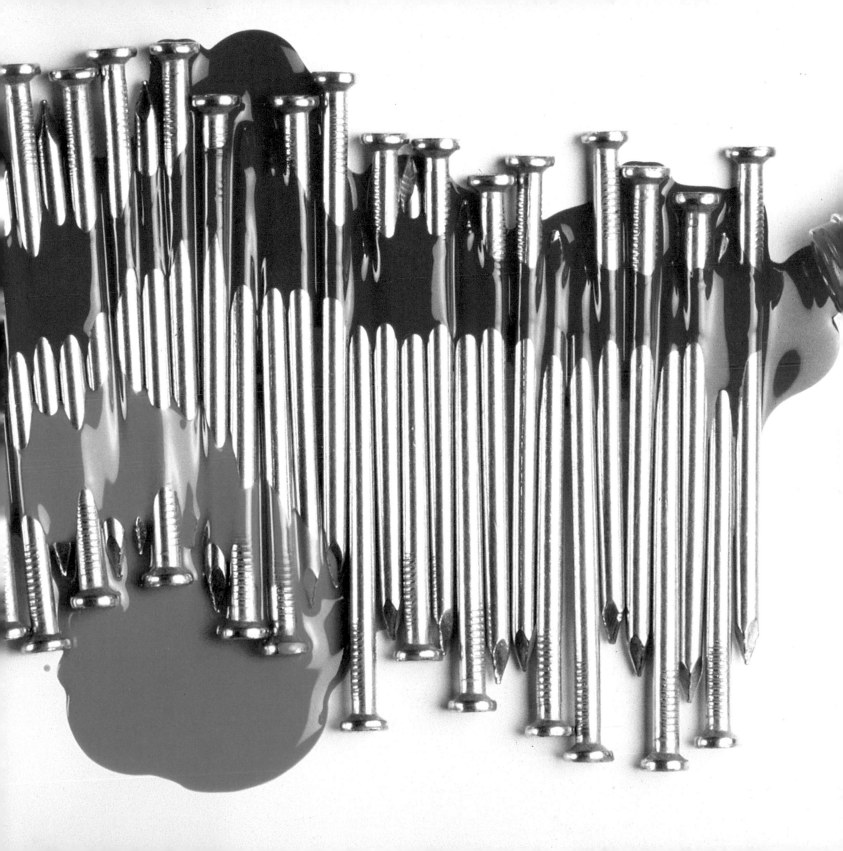

N A I L S

Your hands communicate many of your inner feelings - passion, anger, happiness, rejection and tenderness. Beautifully groomed hands tell the world that you care about yourself.

Normal nails are pink, flexible and strong.

Dry nails are prone to splitting and peeling and may have horizontal ridges. Lack of moisture is often caused by dipping hands into hot water and household detergents. The answer is wear rubber gloves. Frequent swimming in chlorinated water will also dehydrate nails. Before you reach for a nail strengthener, beware that some contain formaldehyde which can take moisture out. Nail oils contain ingredients that will feed the skin around the nails and the cuticle. Keep a hand cream by the sink and apply it every time you wash your hands, particularly during winter months.

Brittle nails are hard, inflexible and can crack or chip. They may curve and have vertical ridges. The overuse of strengtheners and nail polish removers can be the cause. Avoid nail enamel removers that leave the nail white, which indicates that moisture has been stripped out. The nails also become more brittle as we age. They may look thicker, but are actually less able to retain moisture. Very pronounced ridging along the length of the nails can indicate a fungal infection which will need medical treatment.

Damaged nails can be caused by nail extensions where the nail plate has been buffed down. They are dehydrated, soft and lacklustre.

White marks often indicate injury or over-zealous manicuring. Less commonly they can be a sign of zinc deficiency.

Polished Perfection

A weekly home manicure can be achieved in less than 10 minutes if you follow the tips below:

Begin at the little finger of your right hand and work in. Remove all traces of polish, grease or hand cream with an acetone-free remover. Real cotton wool, rather than synthetic, absorbs enamel better and doesn't contain stray fibres that can stick to polish.

Use an emery board, rather than a metal file, to shape the nails and file in one direction only, from the outside in. You should not see-saw backwards and forwards. To shorten your nails, use the coarser side of the emery board. Your choice of nail shape will depend on personal preference and may be influenced by fashion. Shorter nails usually suit a squared-off shape, which also looks sporty.

Apply cuticle remover, massaging it in. Good removers will not only remove the cuticle, but gently exfoliate the surrounding skin and buff the nail. They are often enriched with lemon extract, natural pumice, panthenol, calcium and vitamins A and E. Gently push the cuticles back with the rubber end of a 'hoof' stick and then rinse away with warm water. You should not cut your cuticles, or allow anyone else to do so. Cuticles must be pushed back very gently. It takes a month for damage to show up in the nail.

Nail builder gels can be used after a cuticle remover to strengthen the nails and are painted on with a brush.

A protective base coat will smooth out any ridges, make your polish less prone to chipping and prevent nail staining. Base coats with reinforcing fibre systems also maintain the life of a manicure, and those with Pro-vitamin B5 (panthenol) will help to hydrate and strengthen the nail.

Apply nail enamel next. The brush should be flexible yet manageable, delivering just the right amount of polish.

Apply polish in three strokes, from the base to the tip of the nail, with the first stroke down the centre of the nail and the other two along either side. Leave a small gap at the sides of the nail. Allow the first coat to dry properly, then apply a second.

Look out for nail enamels that contain calcium, panthenol and polyacrylics, all of which will give nails added resilience.

Some polishes also have a reinforcing fibre system which provides an interwoven matrix to give the polish added strength and to help prevent chipping. Nail enamels, base and top coats should be formaldehyde-free, as formaldehyde dries the nail and can cause allergies.

Finish with a top coat to give your enamel a high gloss finish and provide extra defence for your manicure.

The French Manicure takes a little practice to achieve yourself. The tip is given two coats of white enamel, then the whole nail is painted with a transparent pink polish. A sheer beige can be used as an alternative colour. Kits are available which contain pre-cut strips to enable you to create a well- defined tip.
The American Manicure incorporates a nearly white tip, which is sheerer than the defined white of the French Manicure, and features a plum tint to the nail.

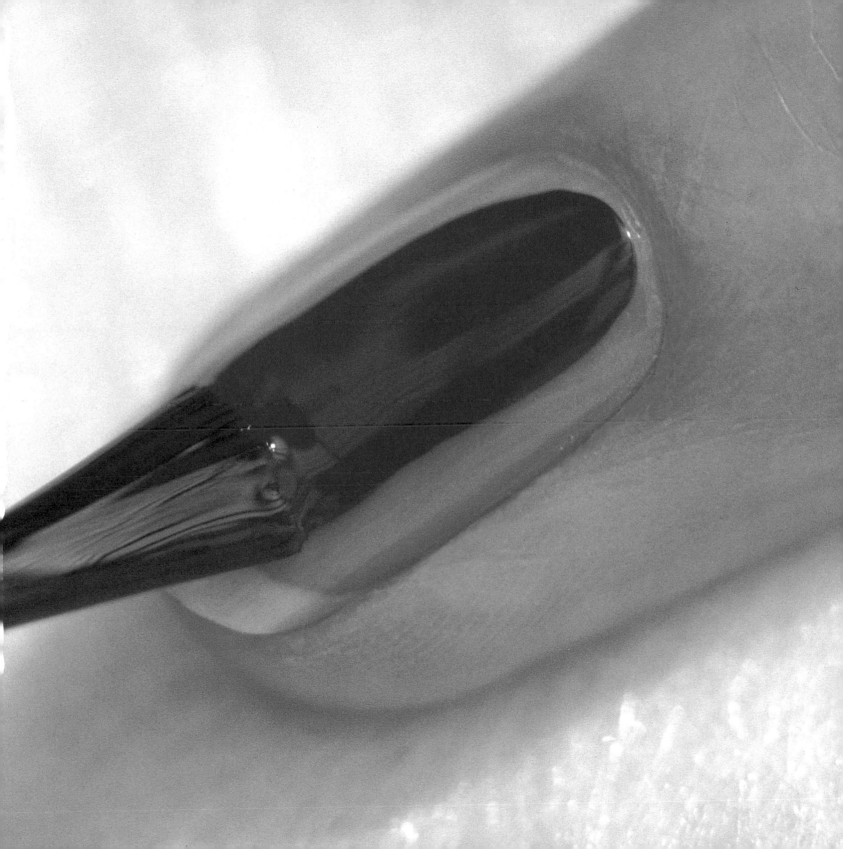

YOUR COLOURS

Choose make-up colours to
suit your skin from palettes
specially designed to help you
look your best.

BLONDE BEAUTY

PLATINUM BLONDES Platinum blondes can have a lot of fun when it comes to make-up. Your attention-grabbing white blonde hair often looks best with a pale, cool complexion particularly if you have aqua blue or green eyes, although platinum hair can look equally dramatic against a tanned-looking skin. If your complexion is pale, keep it that way and work with foundations, powders and colour cosmetics from the cool side of the colour spectrum. You can wear pale or dark eyeshadows and liners, or combine the two.

Pale greys, blues and silver, pastel pinks and beige work well, while deep lavender, purple, navy and charcoal are strong choices for sultry, smokey eyes. For the cheeks, look for cool pink, rose-beige and plum blushers and revel in the wide choice of lipsticks that are available in the right tones for you from blue-reds to wine, berry, mauve and cappuccino brown.

GOLDEN BLONDES Your skin and hair have warm, golden tones to them and your eyes are usually blue or green. Cool colours can drain you of colour, so experiment with warmer hues. Sunny beige powder, rather than a translucent one, is a good choice as it will give your skin a soft glow. For your eyes, choose honey brown, light copper, champagne and soft peach. Warm pinks, peach or salmon are complementary cheeks colours, while you can go for hot coral, apricot or peachey-brown for your lips.

OLIVE-SKINNED BLONDES With your olive-toned skin and brown eyes, brown-based shades are always your best bets. Avoid wearing colours that have too much orange in them. Gold, golden browns and gold-flecked khakis are great eye colours for you. Warm peachey-brown or terracotta are good for cheeks and lips, and brown-reds make for chic lips.

BRUNETTE
BEAUTY

BRUNETTES with pale skin tones and light to medium brown hair, whose eyes are green or blue, usually look their best in cool-toned make-up. Remarkable eyes are well worth focussing your attention on and darker colours like moss green, earthy browns and cocoa will bring out their colour. Softer shades that will also suit you include lavender and cool blues.

Cool pinks and plums will create a fashionable look for the face. However, if you have a lot of red or golden highlights in your hair, you may well be able to wear tawny and rosewood cheek and lipcolours, too. These are good choices if you use a tinted moisturiser or have a tan.

Brunettes who have rich brown hair and yellow or olive skins, will look better in warm rather than cool shades. Toffee brown, dark brown and warm olive greens can be used to line and shade the eyes. Rich brown and brown-black mascaras are flattering choices.

Keep to tawny and terracotta blushers, and shade lips with toffee, cinnamon and brown-tinted reds.

RED-HAIRED BEAUTY

You are a very lucky woman. You can choose between wearing warm, earthy tones or vivid, no-holds-barred colours that create a strong impression.

Most make-up artists recommend that you allow your freckles to show through foundation. They are a key beauty feature and part of you. If you have pale red hair, your natural eye partners are warm terracottas, burnished golds and coppery browns. Look at the flecks in your eyes - hazel eyes often have gold and amber highlights - and the paler shades in your hair and colour-match eyeshadows to these.

Chestnut brown mascara is a good colour to use for paler eyes, walnut brown for deeper-coloured eyes. Check that you get the mascara right to the roots of the lashes, which can be pale.

Amber, apricot and chestnut brown blushers give a great-looking glow to the cheeks, and team well with cinnamon, brick and peachey-brown lipcolours.

The hot alternative is to switch to cooler colours for cheeks and eyes and sock it straight to 'em with cherry red, shocking pink or deep bordeaux for the lips. These shades work particularly well if you have vibrant red hair. Dark green and bronze are effective evening eye colours for you.

B L A C K
B E A U T Y

Black women with golden or reddish tones in their hair and gold-toned skin will find that warm colours enhance their natural colouring. For your eyes, pick dark brown or black eyeliners and yellow, gold, golden brown and copper eyeshadows. Use an eyebrow pencil to shade your brows and match them to the darkest colour in your hair.

Warm chestnut shades are cheek-friendly, and browns that have a hint of pink or red, reds that have a tint of brown and gold-flecked coppers and browns are the best lipcolours for you. Sheer, true reds are good, too.

When choosing a foundation bear in mind that darker black skin often has red under-tones. Foundation and powder should make your skin glow. New light-reflecting pigments in some foundations and powders will help with this but be careful with very matte bases which will turn the skin grey - it is better to wear nothing at all.

One item that may prove to be a beauty essential for you is a shadow liner in barely black. Apply it to the top lid and just at the outside edge of the lower lid. Keep lips super-subtle by choosing hues that are just a shade darker than your natural colour. Translucent colours are especially flattering.

If you are going for a satin-bright look at night, then deep blue or aubergine shadows and silver highlighter will work for your eyes. Pick out the colours in your clothes. Outline your lips with a pencil that is one shade darker than your lipcolour, which could be black cherry or a vivid red.

ASIAN BEAUTY

Rich colours will bring out the beauty of red- or yellow-toned Asian complexions. Outline the top lid - and if you like, the bottom lid - with an eye pencil or eyeliner in black, charcoal or a colour such as dark purple, green or midnight blue. Add a toning, deep eyeshadow on the lid or in the crease of the eye, according to the effect you want to achieve.

You have a great advantage in that you can wear make-up that has a slight sheen or a metallic sparkle to it successfully and still look sophisticated, which many other complexion colours can't. Warm coppery brown eyeshadows, for instance, will pick up on golden tones in your skin. Any deep colour that has a gleam will work well.

Honey browns, deep browns and reddy-browns are all good blusher options for you. Look out for formulations that have just a touch of shine to them to give a healthy-looking bloom to the skin. Smart lip choices are clear crimson red, burgundy and glimmering copper.

Gallery owner and catwalk model **Jibby Beane** stands out from the crowd

Ageless Beauty

Today, women rightly expect to be able to look fantastic at every age. A glowing skin, beautifully-groomed hair and nails and expertly-applied make-up are the secrets. Subtly changing the shades, and the make-up techniques and formulations you use, and adapting your hair colour can make you look many years younger.

Fashion designer Edina Ronay and her taking care of personal appearance

actress daughter Shebah believe that
is empowering to women

Photographer
and mother
Clare Park
says that daily
maintenance is
the secret of
looking polished
and groomed

Like your hair, your skin loses some of its natural pigment over time. As a result, colours that suited you a decade ago may now be off-key. On the other hand, you may find that a more dramatic lipstick or eye make-up creates a sophisticated contrast with your new, paler skin. Experiment with new colours periodically, and try altering the balance of your make-up. For instance, you can play up your lipstick and tone down the blusher.

Top make-up artist Sara Raeburn cites a well-moisturised skin and the right concealer and foundation as essential age-defying strategies. "You can apply moisturiser onto a damp skin for greater effect", Raeburn advises. "Eye creams are important too, to minimise the appearance of fine lines or wrinkles, but there is no need for an eye treatment to be greasy". When moisturiser and eye cream have been absorbed, apply a lightweight foundation.

Many women make the mistake of moving to a heavier, more covering foundation as they get older. These can sit in the lines, and so emphasise them. "It is much more attractive to see the skin", says Raeburn. Light-reflecting bases and concealers are good choices, giving a smoother, soft focus look. They also offer anti skin-ageing ingredients to help improve the skin's tone and condition and to protect it from future damage.

It is important that concealer is relatively thin rather than thick and heavy. Apply it wherever the skin looks darker than the surrounding areas.

If your skin has become drier over the years, you may find that a more moisturising foundation than you have used previously is the answer for a complexion that has tight, fine lines.

Firming serums, applied on their own or over a moisturiser before your foundation, can give the skin an added lift.

When it comes to making up the older face, many women find that their eyes in particular call for more definition over time. Top fashion designer Edina Ronay illustrates how applying well-blended eye pencil and shadows and extra mascara give greater emphasis to the eyes.

If your lips have become thinner, applying a lip base or foundation first will help you plumpen them slightly. You can also use a lipliner that matches your lipstick exactly to draw just outside the natural lipline, then fill in the lips with pencil to create a long-lasting base for lipstick, or simply add a clear lipstick or gloss on top.

Very matte cosmetics can look flat on older skins. A much better option is to use sheer blushers, eyeshadows and lipsticks that have a transparency and very subtle luminosity to them.

Make-up that looks as though it is a natural extension of your own skin is the most flattering look at every age. Using good quality brushes to blend helps you achieve this.

Addressing the balance of the colours of your make-up extends to your eyebrows. If your natural hair colour has changed, matching your eyebrows to your hair colour will give your face a more youthful look. Many women have their eyebrows lightened.

You can use make-up to create a personal style statement and to tell others that you are celebrating this time of your life. Gallery owner and Vivienne Westwood model Jibby Beane uses lipstick to great effect, setting a fuchsia pink or rich wine lipstick against her striking, platinum blonde hair.

If you like to wear vividly-coloured clothes, look for lipstick and blusher that belong to the same colour family but are one or two tones lighter.

Harmonious colour matches become even more important for women with grey hair.

MAKE-UP's GREATEST MOMENTS

Hollywood has always understood that when we paint our faces, we reinvent ourselves. Put on a glamorous look - eyeliner, rich red lips, base and powder, matching nails - and we hold ourselves differently. We can even project a more confident, out-going persona.

It's fun to borrow the all-time, great beauty ideas from the past, and then make the look your own by adding a contemporary twist to the picture. On the coming pages, discover the premier elements that defined the looks of each decade and create a make-up revival.

1920's

Heroines of the decade were actresses Clara Bow and Louise Brooks, women who played the screen vamp to perfection. You need to begin by creating mesmerising, monochrome eyes, set against a porcelain pale complexion. Don't hold back with the black kohl and charcoal eyeshadow and outline both the top and bottom lids generously. Take the shadow into the socket line on the top lid and apply lashings of black mascara. Outline your lips into an exaggerated 'Cupid's bow' with a lip pencil and then colour in using a deep, vampire red. A sharp, black bobbed wig will complete the look.

1930's

Jean Harlow, Bette Davis, Carole Lombard and Greta Garbo were hailed as the icons of their time and with their waved and dyed, chin-length hair and precision make-up, their look was far from natural. During the 'Thirties, women plucked their brows into oblivion - not recommended for you - and re-drew them with a spider-thin line. You can groom your eyebrows by plucking stray hairs - from beneath the browline only - and by using an eyebrow pencil and shadow to make a defined arch, taking it out to the side of the face as far as your dare. Adorn your top eyelid with fake eyelashes, the longer the better, and apply a silvery grey or rich gold shadow to the top lid, from lashline to socket line. Your mouth should be painted to a wide, but not full, shape in a glossy shade of orange or red.

1940's

A softer glamour swept in during the 'Forties and was epitomised by Ingrid Bergman and Vivien Leigh. Brunettes and red-heads became the new pin-ups of the day, and leading lights included Dorothy Lamour, Ava Gardner and Rita Hayworth. The fashionable age to look was between 30 and 40 and good grooming was considered essential by every woman. Start by setting your hair into curls and sweeping it up and away from the forehead and pinning it behind the ears. Brows became noticeably heavier during this period, so emphasise them using a pencil and feathery strokes. Apply eye pencil as eyeliner, with a thicker line at the outer edge of the eye and draw a fine line under the eye as well, beginning a little way in from the corner of the eye. Use a mid-brown or grey shadow on the top lid and apply mascara to both top and bottom lashes. Finish by painting a generous mouth, with a rich lipcolour and add lip gloss.

50's

Marilyn Monroe will forever be the icon of the 'Fifties. Self-obsessed she may have been, she nevertheless symbolised the beauty truth that you should be whoever you want to be. Make-up became essential to Marilyn's image. To make a Marilyn eye, apply a thick swish of black, liquid eyeliner to the top lid right from the inner corner out to beyond the outer edge of the eye. A quarter of the way along the lower lid, apply a fine liquid line and take it away from the eye in a straight line as you reach the outer edge. Sweep white eyeshadow onto the top lid and apply a little in the corner of the lower lid. Define the socket line with a grey or lilac shadow and apply false eyelashes to the top lid. Dramatically shade in your eyebrows with pencil and shadow and brush them up afterwards. Paint your mouth crimson, making the top lip at least as full as, and slightly wider than, your lower lip. Using a dark brown eyebrow pencil, make a beauty spot on the left-hand side of your chin. Finish with a head full of jaw-length platinum curls. A wig will lend instant glamour.

60's

Brigitte Bardot started a revolution in the 'Sixties. Young, free - spirited and rebellious her look focused on wide-eyed innocence. Use eyeliner to create a round, rather than elongated, eye shape. Your eyelashes should be long and thickly coated - don't worry if your mascara clumps together as it goes on! Baby blue, creamy shimmering eyeshadow can be used on the top lid, although a semi-matte white is a good alternative. Remember to make a defining line in the socket of the top lid. The full, pouting mouth made a fashionable appearance for the first time this century and was often coloured in soft beige shades called "nude", or pearlised pink.

70's

It was pop culture that wielded a far greater influence on men's and women's appearance than Hollywood in what was the decade of glam rock. David Bowie-esque psychedelic make-up was the order of the day for the pop generation. Let your artistic instincts run riot when you paint on a 'Seventies' face. This is the only time you can get away with rainbow-coloured eyeshadows and "stripey" blusher. Shiny white or cream highlighter is essential. Dust disco glitter onto cheekbones, browbones and nails, and apply plenty of lip gloss over your lipstick. Wear your hair blonde, long, flowing and centre-parted like Abba, or softly layered, Farrah Fawcett-style.

THE BRIDE

Your wedding day is the day when you want to look your absolute best. Yet there will be some tall orders for your make-up. First of all, it's going to be a long day and you won't want your make-up to move around your face. Then there will be lots of emotion, so you may want to think about wearing waterproof formulations. Most important of all, you can't risk having a shiny face in the photographs.

Before you decide to call the whole thing off, here are some golden rules for wedding make-up.

Have a rehearsal beforehand with the make-up artist and hairdresser who will be creating your look, or with a friend who can give you an honest opinion on your make-up if you are doing it yourself. Above all, remember that your face should mirror how you usually look, with just a little more definition.

If you want to give your face a touch of instant sunshine, experiment with a self-tan lotion for the face at least two weeks beforehand. It will last for around four days, so a fortnight will give you enough time to try another shade should you need to.

Fade-away creams are available if the colour is too intense. Remember that, as far as possible, the colour of your face should match that of your body.

Moisturise the skin well before applying your make-up and give it time to be absorbed.

Apply a translucent make-up base which will help to prevent oil breakthrough and shine.

A medium coverage base is a good choice of foundation for most women, as it gives good coverage to the skin while still looking natural. Alternatively, choose a foundation and concealer with light diffusing particles, which will help to minimise the appearance of fine lines. You will need loose powder on top.

Carry your colour theme through from your flowers and head-dress to your make-up, picking out skin-flattering shades from the bouquet.

Avoid make-up that has a lot of shine and shimmer - it doesn't look good in photographs. That means skipping highly pearlised eyeshadows or lipsticks and avoiding shimmering bronzing powders.

Apply blusher before your eye make-up, so that you're not tempted to use too much on your eyes. Dust a small amount of blusher onto your temples as well to give extra shape and warmth to your face.

Bear in mind that strong colours can drain your face of colour if you're wearing a very pale dress. Instead, keep colours fresh and light. Don't go too dark or heavy around your eyes. Neutral colours like soft brown are good for lining the eyes, while an eyeshadow that's close in colour to your blusher will make a good choice.

Use waterproof mascara, curling your eyelashes first. Define your eyebrows.

Apply lip pencil all over the lips underneath your lipstick. Layer your lipstick, applying one coat, blotting with a tissue and then following with a second coat. Apply a lip fix on top.

Give your chief bridesmaid your powder compact and lipstick to carry.

A French manicure, with perfect white tips and translucent pink, peach or beige enamel is the ideal choice for your nails.

WORKING WOMAN

There's no debate. Make-up can ensure that you are taken seriously at work. Psychologists report that women who wear make-up are seen by those around them as being more confident and capable than women who don't.

A professional environment often has its own sartorial rules, and make-up plays a pivotal part. It is important that your clothes, hairstyle and choice of cosmetics strike the right note. In some offices, scarlet red lipstick, for example, probably isn't going to convey as professional a message as a coffee-coloured one. You can ensure your appearance speaks for you.

Smart women wear a little base. A two-in-one powder creme foundation evens out the complexion, but won't make you look heavily made-up. It is also convenient for retouching during the day. If you have an oily T-zone, you may want to add a little extra powder on top. Then apply the minimum of matte powder blusher, following the line of the cheekbones.

Keep eye colours neutral and matte or semi-matte. Go for taupe, brown, beige, peach or grey eyeliners and shadows and apply in the socket line. Dark colours on the lid can make the eyes look smaller. Define your eyebrows, choose a semi-matte or matte lipstick in muted tones, such as caramel brown, apricot, beige or rosewood. Add a little gloss on top if you wish.

Keep nails short, squared-off and in low-key colours. 'Nude' colours are the easiest to maintain and won't show the chips.

THE WEEKEND

At the weekend you probably want to look healthy and natural, perhaps as though you are wearing practically no make-up at all. The aim is to give your skin that just-out-of-the-shower look and your lips a soft gleam.

If you want to even out your complexion, apply a foundation and powder-in-one with a latex sponge onto a well-moisturised skin. It will give your skin a velvety bloom. Don't forget to touch a little onto your eyelids, too.

Use a tinted moisturiser if you have normal to dry skin, or bronzing pearls on a well-moisturised face if your skin is combination or oily (this is because tinted moisturiser can pool in open pores). Add a little powder if you feel you need it. Women with black skins need only apply plenty of moisturiser, plus a little powder.

Look for moisturisers and tinted moisturisers that have ultraviolet filters and consider applying a high factor sunscreen if you are going to be gardening, sailing or following other outdoor pursuits. Your make-up, too, can offer some sun protection if it contains UV screens.

Apply a touch of blusher to the cheeks and the faintest touch to the browbone, just beneath your eyebrows, to open up the eyes and on your temples and chin.

Use a sheer lipstick in a colour that is close to your own lipcolour, straight from the tube. Dab your first finger over it afterwards if you want it to look super-natural. If your lips tend to be dry, smooth on a little lip balm and leave it for a few minutes. Wipe off any excess before you apply lipstick.

To give your eyes definition, use an eye pencil in an earthy colour close to the top lashes, smudging the line to blend it.

Add two coats of mascara, using a comb to ensure that none of the lashes clump together. That's all you need.

PARTY GIRL

It's time to put a spin on your usual look. There's nothing like showing up at a party looking like a million dollars to give your ego a boost and to turn friends' heads. The secret is to think about how you can look very different.

So: If you usually wear your hair down, you could slick it back or put it up ☆ Is your hair straight? Then why not curl it with styling lotion and heated or velcro rollers, add a hairpiece, or wear a wig? ☆ Do what thousands of women do and head to your hairdresser beforehand for a completely new look ☆ When it comes to your face, have your friends ever seen you with false eyelashes, heavily lined eyes, defined brows and pastel lips? ☆ Or how about with golden, sheeny skin from top to toe (straight from a bottle), cream blusher and sheer red lips, topped with gloss? ☆ Alternatively, there's film starlet matte make-up, well dusted with loose powder with smouldering eyes lined in liquid black eyeliner and vampish wine-coloured lipstick with matching nail enamel.

How to party with staying power

Begin with a translucent make-up base, which will both moisturise the skin and prevent oil breakthrough.

Try applying two light coats of matte or semi-matte foundation, allowing the first coat to dry before adding the second. Press on some loose powder, fluff off excess with a brush and you should stay superbly shine-free.

Remember to apply shadow concealer above the eyes, as well as below them. It provides a base for your eyeshadow and will hide the tiny purple veins there. Applying concealer with a small, firm brush gives an even finish. Choose a concealer that is formulated especially for the area, as it will contain skin-smoothing and moisturising ingredients. Concealers designed for blemishes tend to have a drier texture.

Crease-resistant eyeshadows in velvety textures glide onto the skin and need minimum maintenance. However, you may prefer to stick to eye pencil or eyeliner instead.

Use a lipstick that is designed to hang on in there for as long as you do. Long-lasting lipsticks often contain a lipstain called eosin to give colour that will last for hours at a time.

Use a waterproof mascara (but check you have a suitable remover at home first).

Before you collapse into bed, remove your make-up and apply a moisturiser with revitalising powers that will help you look as though you've had some beauty sleep when you wake up, and an eye gel to alleviate puffiness.

You may well look pale and even years older the next morning, and it won't just be the after-effects of champagne. Your body automatically directs the blood supply away from the skin to more 'vital' organs when you are short of sleep, leaving you looking tired and drawn. Splash cold water on your face to improve circulation and try to get some fresh air and exercise. Apply a tinted moisturiser to conceal the worst.

APPLY A LIQUID HAIR SERUM THAT CONTAINS SILICONE TO THE TOPS OF SHOULDERS AND THE ARMS, YOUR CLEAVAGE AND THE SHIN BONES TO GIVE YOUR SKIN A SUBTLE GLEAM.

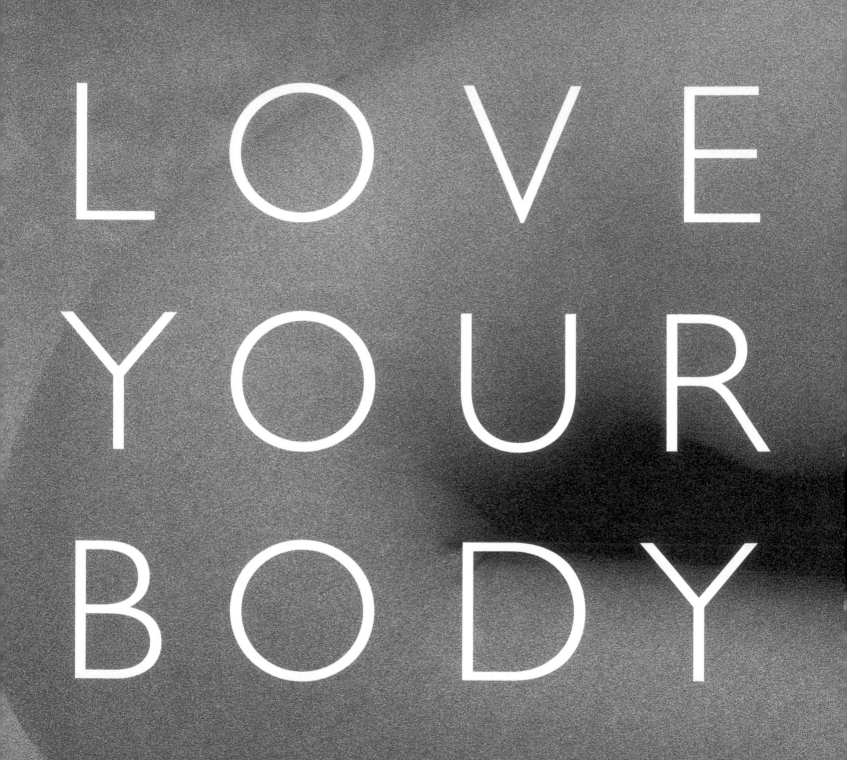

Are you naturally curvy and voluptuous, or superslim and lean? You may want to improve on the body that nature gave you, but you can't drastically change it. Recognising your natural body shape is the first step towards enhancing it.

APPLES & PEARS

We are all predisposed to be one of three body builds.

ECTOMORPHS are lean, even **'string beans'**. For them, building, strengthening and defining muscle tone is an important part of any exercise programme. At the gym, for instance, ectomorphs should use comfortably heavy weights and perform fewer repetitions.

MESOMORPHS are much more muscular, with medium to large bones and quite a curvy shape. Their fitness aim is to burn off excess fat while avoiding becoming overly bulky and muscular. Mesomorphs should avoid training with heavy weights.

ENDOMORPHS are more box-shaped and have a tendency to be chubby. A consistent aerobic regime is the key and if you are using an exercise cycle, set it at a low resistance so that your muscles do not become bulky. Use light weights in the gym.

As well as being one of three natural body builds, your body is also geared to one of two kinds of fat distribution. If you tend to put weight on around your stomach, you are termed an **"apple"**. If you are heavier around the hips and thighs, you are a **"pear"**.

Women and men whose bodies have become apple-like have been shown in studies to be at increased risk of diabetes and heart disease. Losing the excess fat is all important. Women are more likely to be pear-shaped, while men deposit fat apple-style, although as we age, we tend to store more of our fat around the waist and stomach.

BODY

MAINTENANCE

Regular exercise is the key to a longer, healthier life. But how do you stick to a programme? Research has found that being given precise targets and encouragement by a fitness instructor is one answer. In a recent study, one group of women were guided in each session by an instructor, while another group set their own goals. Nearly three-quarters of the women in the instructor-led group achieved their target, while less than a quarter of the women in the self-motivated group were able to match their colleagues' results.

How much exercise do you need, and of what type?

Aerobic exercise (which means "with air") burns oxygen and fat for fuel. It increases your cardiovascular (heart and lungs) endurance and needs to be done at the right intensity for your individual fitness level and your age (an instructor will calculate this for you). You should be slightly out of breath while exercising aerobically, but still able to hold a conversation. Done regularly, vigorous aerobic exercise like brisk walking, running (treadmills are a better bet than the pavement), cycling and using a stairclimber can cut your risk of a heart attack in half. By improving blood flow to the muscles and to the brain, you combat feelings of lethargy. You need to do at least 20 minutes of aerobic exercise, three to five times a week.

Weight-bearing exercise is particularly important for women because it 'builds' bone, and so helps to reduce the risk of osteoporosis, a condition which affects women after the menopause, and which makes bones brittle. A combination of aerobic exercise that is weight-bearing such as walking, working out with weights and floor exercises, should be included in your workout programme two to three times a week.

Muscle-toning exercises using resistance equipment in the gym, circuit training and floor exercises will strengthen your muscles, maintain good posture and counteract the body's tendency to lose muscle mass from the age of 30 onwards. Incorporate them into your aerobic and weight-bearing regime.

Stretching exercises ensure that you balance strength with flexibility and should be done at the beginning of your workout, after your body has warmed up, and at the end of the session.

It is possible to exercise without really trying

If you sit at a desk for long periods of time, combat a slumped posture by sitting well back in the chair and lifting up from the solar plexus (which is sited just above your navel). Take your arms out to the side, and with your fists closed circle your arms backwards slowly 20 times. You will be able to feel the muscles in your upper back working.

Good Posture
is the backbone of beauty.

The Alexander Technique was developed by an actor, Frederick Alexander, who found that we unconsciously store tensions in our bodies and subsequently develop postural problems and ways of using our bodies that can have far-reaching effects on our well-being. Lessons with an Alexander Teacher can make a vast difference to how you move, sit and stand. For instance, many of us tend to throw or pull our heads back when standing up or performing other actions, which places a great deal of strain on our neck muscles. When standing up from a chair, wait until your body weight is over your feet before rising, if necessary bringing your feet back first. Check that you are not leaning forward when you are writing, typing or eating, as this affects your breathing and therefore your energy levels.

BATHTIME BLISS

Lie back, take a deep breath and just let go.
It is remarkable what a little
liquid refreshment
can do for
you.

All you need is: * A body scrub * A natural bristle brush with a long handle and a massage mitt * Bath gel, foam or salts * A conditioning body lotion * A body spray * A neck pillow, such as a travel pillow * Candles, soothing music and a book or magazine * Eye pads * Warm towels, a bathrobe and slippers

Why not take **15 minutes** out to indulge in the relaxing ritual of bathing this evening? First, create an environment that is conducive to relaxation. Switch on some **soothing music** in the next room, light some candles and position them around the bath. Find a good book or magazine and turn the answerphone on.

Run a warm bath (don't have it too hot or your heart rate will increase and you could find it hard to sleep later) and pour a spa-inspired bath gel or salts into the water. Some contain sea minerals and sea kelp to **purify the skin**, while others include relaxing or invigorating essential oils. Dip down into the bath and stand up again so that you can apply a body scrub to damp skin. **Massage it in well** using circular motions and use

a long-handled natural bristle brush to get to hard-to-reach areas, remembering to brush **towards the heart**. Use a toning mitt gently on hips, thighs and around the knees, areas which are prone to **sluggish circulation** and cellulite. Rinse off and relax onto the neck pillow.

Now is a good chance to apply eye pads for a few minutes, or to reach for your book. **Soak for 10 minutes**.

Pat your skin gently with the **warm towels** and apply body lotion to slightly damp skin, to seal in extra moisture. If you want to feel **energised** as well as **revitalised**, apply a body spray with natural extracts of sea minerals and rehydrating agents all over your body.

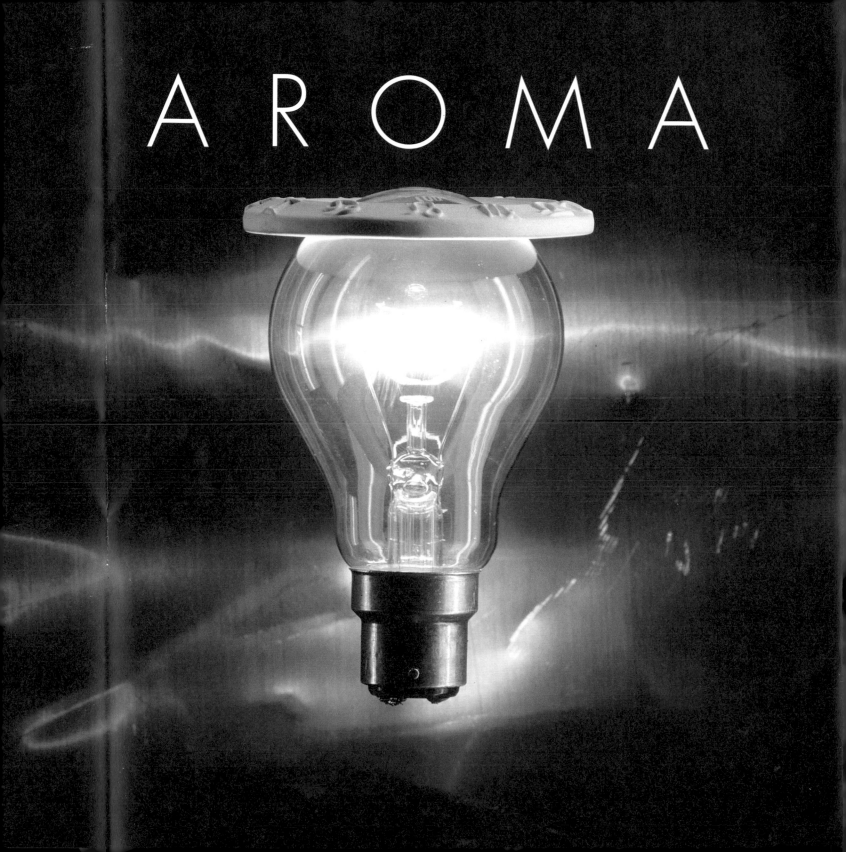

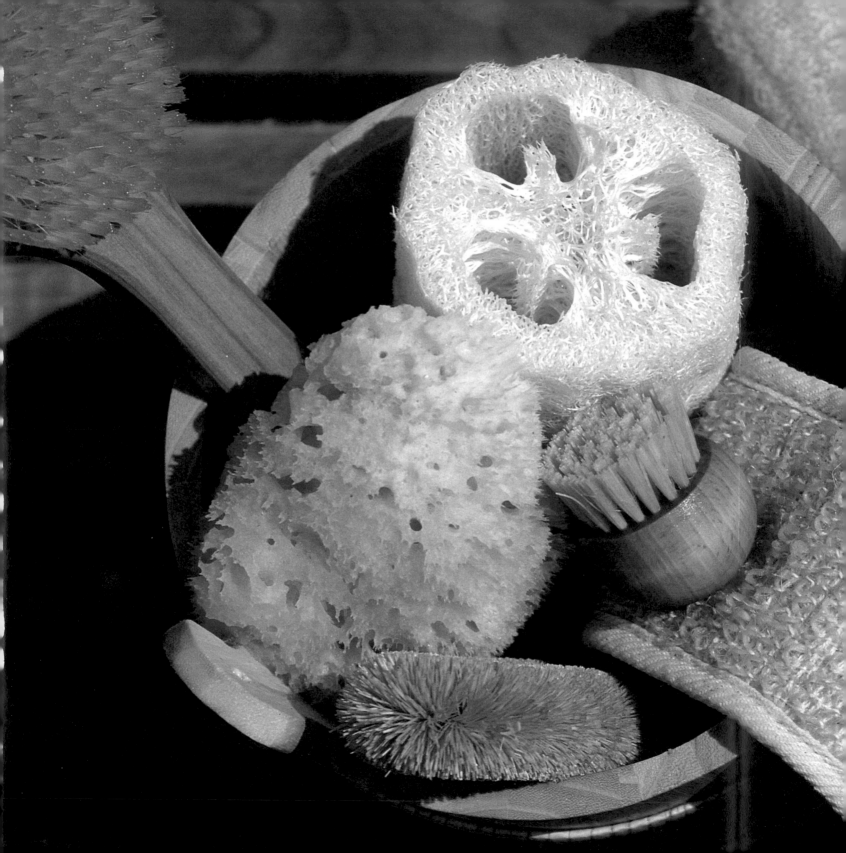

THERAPY

Relaxing and soothing, revitalising and refreshing, mood-boosting and sensuous...essential oils, extracted from plants and herbs, offer therapeutic benefits for both your body and mind.

Aromatherapy is a powerful, natural treatment that uses the oils found in a range of plants. The highly-scented molecules travel straight to the emotional centre of your brain, as well as passing into the bloodstream.

Trained aromatherapists mix blends of essential oils to treat a range of conditions. You can use essential oils yourself at home, by buying undiluted oils and mixing them with a 'carrier oil' for massage, adding them to your bath or scenting your environment. You can also buy ready-blended products, which incorporate a number of different oils diluted in a carrier oil, formulated to treat specific conditions.

Certain oils, in particular camphor, hyssop, parsley, pennyroyal and sage, cannot be used if you are pregnant. Consult your doctor or a trained aromatherapist if you are pregnant, epileptic or have high blood pressure, or if you wish to use the oils on children. You should not massage somebody who has a temperature.

Neither essential oils nor blends should be taken orally. Most oils should not be used neat on the skin (although lavender can be applied neat to burns and tea tree oil can be dabbed onto spots and cold sores) and do not be tempted to use more than the recommended amounts whichever method you are using.

DOING IT FOR YOURSELF

Massage: For a full body massage, add 20 drops of an essential oil to 50ml of a carrier oil such as grapeseed or sweet almond. For facial massage, add two drops to 5ml (one teaspoon) of carrier oil. You can also add one to two drops of essential oil to an unscented moisturiser.

Bathing: Add six to eight drops of essential oil to your bath and swirl around to disperse. Close the door and windows and soak for 10 minutes so that the oil can be absorbed through the skin.

Inhaling: Put two to four drops on a tissue and inhale deeply. You can place the tissue on a saucer by your bed to aid a good night's sleep. For colds, a congestion-easing oil can be added to a bowl of hot water and inhaled with a towel over your head. Breathe deeply. Essential oils should not be inhaled directly from the bottle.

Compress: This method can be used where somebody has a temperature and so should not be massaged. Soak a towel or fabric in tepid water, wring it out and sprinkle with a few drops of your chosen oil. Apply to the forehead or stomach.

Environment: To scent a room, relax or energise you, or to act as an antiseptic when cold and flu germs are around, perfume your surroundings using a vaporiser. Electric and candle vaporisers are widely available, as are ceramic rings, which can be filled with oil and placed onto a light bulb before switching it on.

ESSENTIAL OIL	PROPERTIES	RENOWNED FOR	TRY IT
CAMOMILE	Calming, mood-lifting, soothing, comforting	There are three different types of Camomile available - Roman Camomile is best for stress problems, while German Camomile is best for helping the skin. Both are very expensive. Moroccan Chamomile is the budget version and has general calming and uplifting properties.	As a massage oil, in the bath or on a tissue.
CLARY SAGE	Warming and relaxing. It is also antispasmodic and said to be an aphrodisiac.	Helping to ease PMS, period pains, stomach ache, stress and general aches and pains.	In the bath or as a body massage.
EUCALYPTUS	Strongly antiseptic and decongestant.	Helping with chest problems. Clears the catarrh of coughs and colds, and eases sinus problems and bronchitis.	Inhaled from a bowl of hot water or on a tissue.
GERANIUM	Fortifying and uplifting, geranium is also analgesic, astringent and diuretic.	Soothing eczema, dermatitis, inflammation and blotchiness. Calming the digestive system. Also has a regulating effect on hormones, it is especially helpful in treating PMS and problems associated with the menopause. Eases fatigue and panic attacks.	In the bath, as a facial oil or in a steamer as part of a facial.
JUNIPER	Stimulating, refreshing, antiseptic, astringent, detoxifying.	Stimulating the kidneys to fight fluid retention, cystitis and cellulite (its detoxifying benefits also help to relieve hangovers). Controlling oily skin problems, acne, dandruff and scalp problems.	In the bath or as a general massage oil, particularly on the hips and thighs for cellulite.
LAVENDER	Antiseptic, healing, calming, soothing, pain relieving.	Helping to heal and soothe sore skin, sunburn, spots, bruises, chilblains, burns, bites and infections. Easing general aches and pains. Relieving insomnia, headaches, anxiety and other forms of stress, including panic attacks and nightmares.	Applied directly to burns, or diluted (one drop lavender oil in 1ml of sweet almond oil) for localised treatment. Use in the bath and inhale from a tissue.

ESSENTIAL OIL	PROPERTIES	RENOWNED FOR	TRY IT
NEROLI (also known as orange blossom)	Deeply relaxing, yet uplifting. Neroli is a very expensive oil so you will find that it is frequently sold ready diluted	Soothing dry and sensitive skin, it is also reputed to help relieve anxiety, panic and shock, assist sleep and ease PMS.	As a facial oil or in your bath at night to help stress and beat insomnia. Inhale from a tissue for immediate calming benefits. Fight PMT with six drops in the bath every day for one week before your period is due.
PEPPERMINT	Cooling, refreshing, clearing.	Easing an upset stomach and travel sickness. Clearing congestion caused by colds, coughs and sinus problems. Helping headaches and migraines. Stimulating and refreshing the mind and body. Combatting bad breath.	In a vaporiser or inhaled from a tissue. As a mouthwash, dilute two drops in half a pint of water.
ROSE	Soothing, relaxing, comforting and a general tonic. Rose oil is very expensive and is often sold ready-diluted.	Helping with skin problems like eczema, dryness and puffiness. Soothing an upset stomach and nausea. Easing depression. Helping to prevent stretchmarks.	With almond oil as a facial treatment. To soften dry skin on the feet, add four drops to a footbath. Mix one drop with three drops of sandalwood in 10ml almond oil and stroke in daily to prevent stretchmarks. Can also be used in the bath or as a room fragrance.
ROSEMARY	Invigorating, refreshing, stimulating to the mind and body.	Easing lethargy. Good for digestive ailments, cellulite, fluid retention and dandruff.	As a room freshener. Help to boost concentration by inhaling it from a tissue. Never use neat rosemary oil on the skin.
TEA TREE	Antiseptic, fungicidal, anti-inflammatory, bactericidal.	Soothing itching, spots, cold sores and for treating fungal infections like athlete's foot, dandruff and thrush. Avoid if you have very sensitive skin.	Using one or two drops on a cotton bud and dabbing directly onto individual spots or cold sores. In the bath for thrush.
YLANG YLANG	Sedative, sensual, aphrodisiac.	Easing tension and hormonal problems. Relieving insomnia.	In the bath, as a massage oil or room fragrance.

REFLEXOLOGY

Five thousand years ago, the ancient Chinese knew a thing or two about encouraging the body to heal itself and one of their skills was reflexology. Today it is one of the most popular complementary therapies.

Reflexology was revived at the beginning of this century by an American ear, nose and throat specialist who called it "zone therapy" and who proved that by applying pressure to one part of the body you could anaesthetize another, related area.

The 1980s saw a huge surge of public interest in this and other forms of alternative therapies, and there are now approximately 3,000 trained reflexologists practising in the U.K.

The underlying philosophy of reflexology - and of acupuncture and the Japanese pressure point massage known as shiatsu - is that energy channels, called meridians or zones, which pass through the organs of the body, all end in the feet.

There are 7,000 nerve endings in the feet and by using special massage techniques on particular areas, you can work on corresponding areas of the body. Mapping the energy zones of the feet is surprisingly logical. For instance, the big toe relates to the head, the balls of the feet represent the shoulders and chest, and the narrow instep of the foot is linked to the waist.

Reflexology works by helping to stimulate the body's natural healing processes. It is deeply relaxing and is especially useful for easing stress-related problems such as tiredness, digestive problems, insomnia, migraine, eczema and allergies. Although it offers benefits across the health spectrum, it does not claim to diagnose specific illnesses or to be a medical treatment.

A professional reflexology session lasts about 45 minutes and begins with a light foot massage to help you relax. Methodical examination of all reflex points follows, with the therapist working with his or her thumbs and usually beginning with the big toe and working outwards across the foot and gradually down to the heels.

The backs of the heels, both sides and the tops of each foot should also be included. Although the pressure is consistent, when a problem point is found, the difference can be felt by both the patient and the practitioner. This can vary from a sensation of increased pressure, to a sharp, pricking feeling as though gravel or the therapist's thumbnail is being pressed into the flesh.

Changes in sensation are due to the presence of crystalline deposits at the nerve-endings, indicating stress or imbalance in the related area of the body. Gently breaking them up through massage helps to resolve the problem.

Sensations of tenderness can in some instances be due to a problem with the foot's structure, a bruise, bunion or corn, rather than indicating that something is out of synch elsewhere in the body.

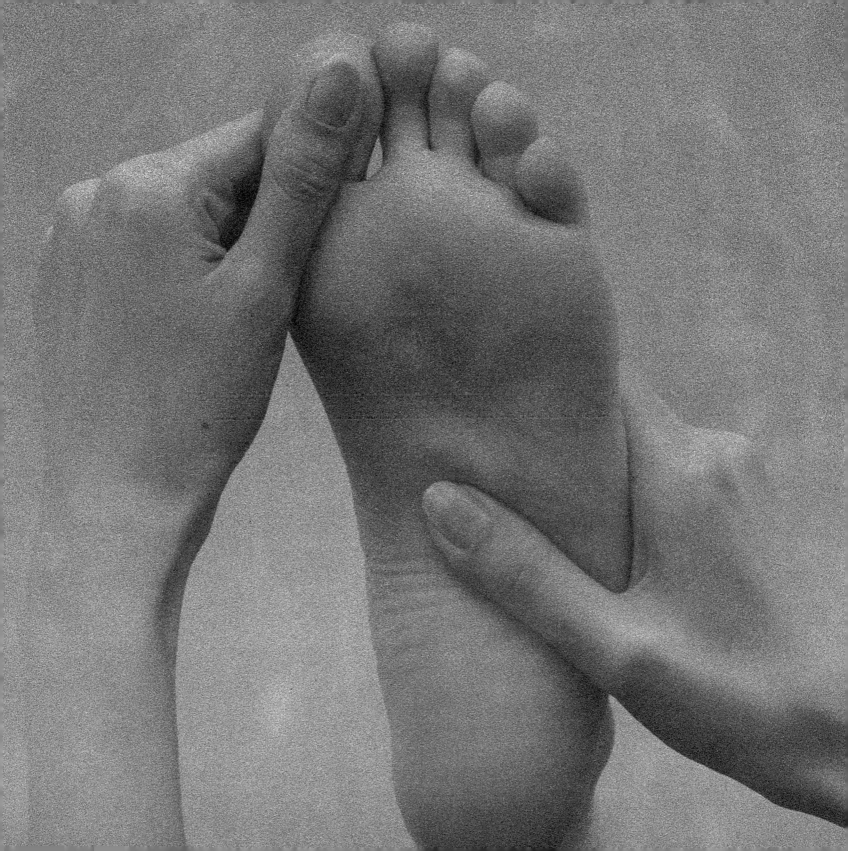

CAN YOU USE REFLEXOLOGY TO HELP YOURSELF?

You can use reflexology on your own feet, but reflexologists have on average one year's training behind them. Techniques employed include thumb and finger walking and thumb pressing and rotation. Different pressures are used on different parts of the foot.

To try it for yourself, get into a comfortable sitting position and concentrate on your breathing for a couple of minutes. Now pull one foot towards your lap. Choose the area you want to work on, and using your thumb, press down and slightly forwards with the pad of your thumb and as you release the pressure, roll the thumb backwards rather than forwards so that you don't press the nail into your foot.

Don't lose contact with your foot as you "loop" over towards the next reflex point. Keep the movements slow, smooth and even.

Avoid pressing directly over varicose veins or swollen areas. Where an area feels grainy, use very light, gentle kneading for a few seconds. Don't over-massage the area. Finish with broad stroking movements, lightly rotating each toe and both ankles in each direction, then gently wringing each foot with both hands.

There are also nerve endings in the hands and in the ears. However, most reflexologists agree that it is the feet that are generally more responsive.

WHEN TO TAKE CARE

Certain medical conditions could mean that you need special care, or they may make reflexology inappropriate. You should tell your practitioner if you are pregnant, taking medication, if you suffer from thrombosis, phlebitis, arthritis in the feet, heart problems or diabetes and you should not use reflexology on yourself if any of these conditions apply to you.

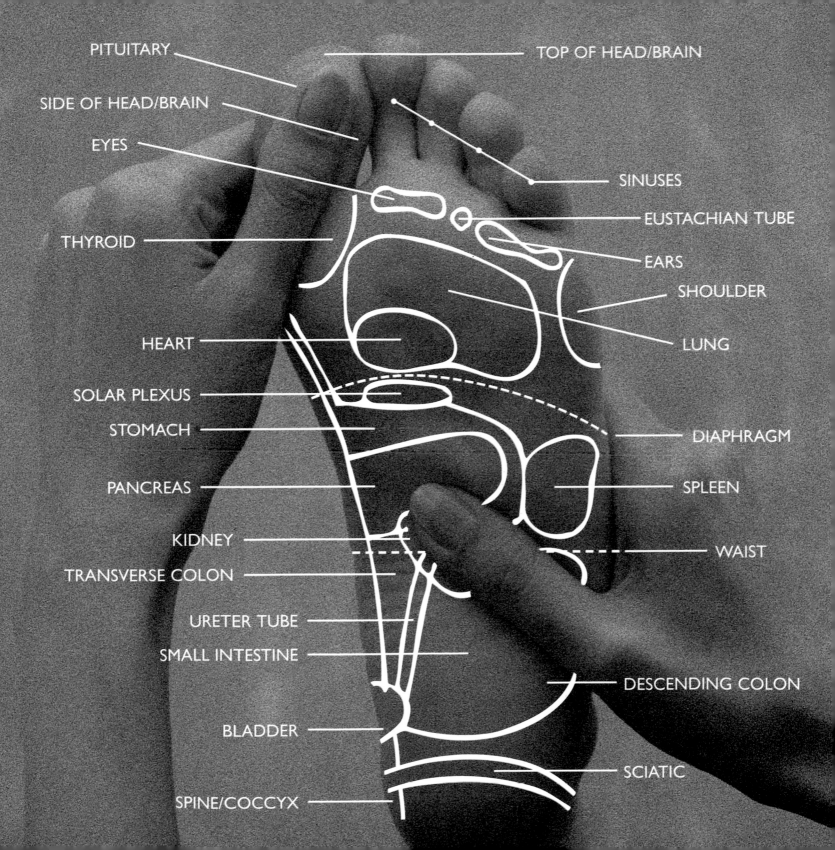

PITUITARY

TOP OF HEAD/BRAIN

SIDE OF HEAD/BRAIN

EYES

SINUSES

EUSTACHIAN TUBE

THYROID

EARS

SHOULDER

HEART

LUNG

SOLAR PLEXUS

STOMACH

DIAPHRAGM

PANCREAS

SPLEEN

KIDNEY

TRANSVERSE COLON

WAIST

URETER TUBE

SMALL INTESTINE

DESCENDING COLON

BLADDER

SCIATIC

SPINE/COCCYX

CELLULITE

As many as 80 per cent of women say that they have cellulite. It's a controversial condition that can be helped, when you know how.

Cellulite. Is it fat or fact? Orthodox medicine may refute the existence of cellulite, but specialists who take a more holistic view argue that the orange peel texture that develops on so many women's thighs and buttocks (and sometimes around the stomach, upper arms and knees, too) is a condition all of its own.

It occurs when the fat cells become saturated with toxic wastes and fluid. Hardened connective fibres may then surround these cells, making the flesh feel lumpy and tender when squeezed. The outward appearance and extent of cellulite varies widely from woman to woman.

Cellulite is believed to be linked to the 'female' hormone oestrogen, which affects fat storage, and to the depositing of toxins in areas where they can do the least damage. The lymphatic system is responsible for the removal of toxins, and if it is sluggish, internal pollution can result. Since the lymph fluid is pushed around the body primarily by the actions of our muscles, lack of exercise will slow down its circulation, leaving you more at risk of developing cellulite.

Cellulite becomes more difficult to treat as it becomes more established, and it worsens with age. Pear-shaped women, and those who put on weight easily, are more prone to develop it.

Your eating
and exercise habits
play a major part
in the development
of cellulite,
and changing them
can improve its
appearance once it
has formed.

1 Eat natural, healthy foods Reduce your intake of caffeine and alcohol, and drink around six glasses of water a day. Watch your consumption of fat, salt and sugar, and of additives and pesticides which encourage retention of toxins in the cells.

2 Exercise Aerobic exercise will improve lymph drainage and blood circulation, and muscle toning movements will firm flabby flesh, where toxins and fluid are prone to gather.

3 Brush your body Body brushing improves lymph drainage and should be done each day on dry skin, before you step into the bath or shower. Using a long-handled natural bristle brush, make long sweeping movements, working up from the feet towards the heart. Start gently, as your skin will feel sensitive to the scratchy texture of the brush for the first few days.

4 Mitts and creams Massage gloves are effective when used regularly. Massage gently, especially with gloves that have raised rubber beads, or you could break fine capillaries, which will show up as tiny red 'spider' veins. Cellulite creams contain aromatherapy oils and plant extracts such as Butcher's broom, hawkweed, horsetail, ivy and caffeine. These are diuretics, designed to reduce fluid retention. Caffeine and its relative theophylline are believed to be able to increase the metabolism of fat cells, while an amino acid, L-carnitine, is claimed to inhibit fat storage. Improvement should generally be seen within 30 days of continual use.

You will find that a course of treatments is recommended for the following methods and that they can be very expensive. Some of the methods are more established than others. Approach any treatment with caution and if you do consider having them, ask to talk to at least one satisfied former client.

CELLULOLIPOLYSIS Very fine needles are inserted into the skin and electric current is passed through them. It has been described by some women as painful, and should be medically supervised.

G5 MASSAGE A vibrating pad is moved over the cellulite-prone zones. The skin can be red and itchy afterwards. Widely available in beauty salons and health spas.

IONITHERMIE Gels, then a warm clay, are applied and electrodes are inserted between the layers to conduct galvanic current (increasing absorption of the products) and faradic current (exercising the muscles). You will feel a tingling sensation followed by stronger muscle contractions. Some women find the experience relaxing, while others say that it is uncomfortable. Offered in beauty salons.

LIPOSUCTION This form of cosmetic surgery is probably the most extreme treatment for cellulite. It is principally designed to suck out fat and may not necessarily change the texture of the skin. The bruising can be very severe and as with all operations, it carries risks.

THALASSOTHERAPY Seawater and seaweed therapy is widely used in health spas across France to treat a range of health problems and is increasingly available in Britain. Treatment for cellulite includes the use of warm seawater jets which are moved up and down the hips and thighs by a therapist, hydrotherapy 'massage' baths, seaweed body wraps and cellulite creams.

BODY WORKSHOP

New body treatments that work fast to make you feel and look a whole lot better are now catching our attention. Whether you want to make a few home improvements or decide to head to a beauty salon for the professional touch, the body shapers here are well worth considering.

BODY SCRUBS These quick and easy body boosters can give you baby-soft skin in seconds. By lifting away dead surface cells, you permit other treatments such as body masks, moisturisers and cellulite creams to act more effectively. Body exfoliators are massaged onto damp skin using a circular action and then simply rinsed off. Essential oils and seaweed extracts are some of the ingredients that are often included to provide added skin benefits. Use a body scrub twice a week and follow up with body lotion.

SPA BATHS Specially harvested seaweed, mineral spa mud and Dead Sea salts are all available to create a restorative and therapeutic bath at home or at a health hydro. Bubbling baths are optional; the treatment is then known as hydrotherapy. You can still obtain good results without the Jacuzzi-effect.

With some of the products you have to be prepared to give the bath a clean afterwards! Dead Sea salts contain 25 minerals including bromide which is reputed to be relaxing.

BODY MASKS They are designed to improve tone and firmness and will also impart softness. You need to be able to walk around your home in private if you're going to try this treatment. Masks are applied from the neck downwards. Some work in two to three minutes, while others are left on for 20 minutes or more, before being rinsed off. Ingredients include seaweeds, which are claimed to have a reviving and detoxifying action, plant extracts with skin toning properties, and hydrating agents to smooth the skin.

CONTOUR WRAPS If you don't mind being shrink-wrapped in cling film for an hour or mummified in wet bandages, a body wrap treatment could be for you. They can be done professionally at a beauty salon, or are available as home kits, but read the instructions carefully. The idea is to compress the tissues and so to encourage excess fluid to be flushed out from the cells. A body mask is applied before the wrapping material and, in some cases, the bandages are soaked in mud. Thankfully, it is warm.

Bear in mind that measurements taken before and after a contour wrap treatment may indicate that you have lost an impressive number of inches, but you will still have the body fat that you started with.

Refer to Cellulite Treatments for details of other inch-loss and toning treatments such as Ionithermie.

R - E - L - A - X

If you feel as though you are living your life inside a pressure cooker, it's time you took control.

Stop for a moment and think about how your body feels. Is it free of muscular tension? Do you feel contented? Or are you strung-up, anxious and forever trying to achieve more than is humanly possible?

When you switch on the "fight-or-flight" response of stress, your heart rate, breathing rate and blood pressure all increase, adrenalin rushes around the body, muscles tense up ready for action and hormone production changes. If your body is constantly on red alert, your well-being and your health will eventually be affected.

Not all stress is a bad thing, of course. Getting married, being promoted and going on holiday all register on the stress scale, but provide excitement and enjoyment in your life.

We all respond differently to stress. Often we do not realise that stress, or an inability to relax, is at the source of the way we are feeling (check the stress signals below).

Recognising and reducing the effects of stress is important, and many of us need to learn how to relax. Flopping into a chair is probably not enough, especially if you do not have time for physical exercise. Over the page, you will find a variety of ways to make regular relaxation a part of your lifestyle.

The following signs indicate that you may be suffering the effects of stress.
Physical symptoms, in particular, should be checked with your doctor.

How your body feels or reacts
1. Butterflies in the stomach
2. Fast or irregular heartbeat
3. Muscular tension or pain
4. Trembling
5. Headaches
6. Changes in vision
7. Breathlessness
8. Blushing
9. Disturbed or excessive sleep
10. Adult acne, eczema or psoriasis
11. Digestive problems
12. Tiredness or exhaustion
13. Hair loss in women

Moods and Emotions
1. Unhappiness
2. Feelings of depression or hopelessness
3. Feeling overwhelmed
4. Aggressive behaviour or outbursts
5. Withdrawal
6. Boredom or apathy
7. Emotionality or tearfulness
8. Lack of self-confidence
9. Anxiety or fear
10. Irritability
11. Loss of libido
12. Lack of interest or enjoyment in life

How you think and act
1. Lack of concentration
2. Forgetfulness
3. Preoccupation
4. Inability to think about alternative options
5. Persistant negative thinking
6. Overactivity
7. Constant hurrying, lateness or over-commitment
8. Excessive drinking or smoking
9. Use of drugs
10. Loss of appetite or over-eating
11. Weight change

THE R-E-L-A-X

Telling yourself to relax is so much easier than actually doing it. Stress has many sources - health, relationships, work, finances, to name just a few. You may need to make some changes to your daily routine in order to find the time for a de-stressing activity or a specific relaxation technique, and don't kid yourself - it takes commitment to break long-standing bad habits.

Feel the rhythm Get up at the same time each day and, whenever possible, go to bed at around the same time each night. Your body clocks like regularity.

Get physical. Both vigorous forms of exercise, such as aerobics, cycling, brisk walking or tennis, and relaxing forms such as stretching, swimming, yoga and T'ai Chi, reduce muscular tensions and help to restore your equilibrium.

Set aside some time Escape with a good book, have a long aromatherapy bath, book a massage or take up a creative hobby.

Take regular breaks during the day Get outside at lunchtime and go for a short walk and you will find that you will have more energy to see you through the afternoon.

Learn when to say no Establish your personal priorities and be decisive with others.

Breathe deeply When you are under stress, you tend to breathe shallowly. At the start of the evening, sit quietly in a chair or lie down somewhere comfortable and rest your hands on your diaphragm, (just below your ribs) with your fingers touching. Close your eyes and breathe in slowly and deeply through your nose. Your fingers should move up and apart. Hold the breath for a few moments, then breathe out through your mouth or nose. Repeat three or four times, then breathe naturally.

Meditation The principle of meditation is that it gives the mind the opportunity to rest. You can try it for yourself, or be taught how to meditate by an expert. You need to set aside 20 minutes. Lie or sit somewhere where you will not be disturbed and pick a word, known as a mantra, that has no special relevance. The word "one" is popular. Close your eyes and focus on your breathing. Repeat your mantra as you breathe and simply allow other thoughts that enter your mind to

float away. As you begin to relax, you may notice that you swallow more often and that your digestive system starts to "gurgle".

Progressive muscle relaxation Relaxation tapes, set to soothing music, are a great way to practice progressive muscle relaxation, taking you through each stage step-by-step. Lie down on a firm bed or on the floor, with a pillow or cushion under your head and knees. Let your hands rest, palms up, by your sides or place them on your stomach. Allow your feet to fall outwards and your body to sink into the floor. Unclench your teeth and relax your face and neck. Breathe slowly throughout. Working up the body, begin by scrunching the toes and muscles in the feet. Hold for a few seconds, then simply let go, imagining that your feet feel warm and heavy. Repeat with the calf muscles, then the whole of the right leg, followed by the left leg. Clench your buttocks and let go, then do the same with your stomach muscles. Progress to your right hand, holding it in a tight fist then let go, repeat with your left hand. Hunch your shoulders up to your ears then relax them. Rock your head gently from side to side. Yawn widely and let go. Scrunch up your eyes and let go. Concentrating on how warm and peaceful you feel, rest in this position for 5 minutes or more and allow yourself to come to slowly.

BODY SLEEKERS

Attitudes to body hair vary from culture to culture. It is because hairiness is a masculine trait that women in some societies long for sleek, smooth legs and arms.

METHOD	REGROWTH TIME	MINIMUM EFFORT, MAXIMUM EFFECT
Shaving: for legs and under arms.	Regrowth time: Up to five days (but don't be surprised if you see the start of new hair the next day)	Allow warm water to swell the hairs for a few minutes before you begin, then use a shaving gel or foam. Use a razor with a comb guard and take your time - that way you will avoid nicks. If you are going to the beach or pool, shave the evening before as chlorine and sunscreens could cause irritation. Moisturise legs afterwards as shaving removes some of the surface layers of skin cells.
Depilatory creams: For facial hair, underarms, legs, and bikini line.	Up to one week. They work by dissolving the hair just below the surface of the skin and the results last longer than shaving.	Do a patch test 24 hours beforehand if you are using a new product and do not use on broken or irritated skin. Formulations especially for sensitive skins are also available.
Waxing: For legs, bikini line and underarms. Hot wax can be used for the face.	Up to four weeks. The wax includes beeswax and paraffin and is either applied warm (the method most used in beauty salons) or cold on ready-coated plastic strips (available as home kits).	The hairs grow back finer after repeated treatments. The skin must be pulled taut before the wax strip is pulled back against the direction of hair growth. Avoid hot showers, the sun, fragrance and deodorant or excess perspiration for the next 24 hours. If in-growing hairs are a problem, use an exfoliator regularly.
Sugaring: For legs, bikini line and underarms.	Up to four weeks.	Well-known in India, a sugar and water putty is applied and used in the same way as waxing.
Epilators: For the legs and the face.	Up to four weeks.	Home epilators use rotating wires or disks to whip out the hair at the root with a tweezer-like action. Settings are adjustable to suit your pain barrier. Some epilators are designed for the legs, others for the face. An epilator can be used on underarm hair, but the skin would need to be pulled very tight as the hair is very strong and removal therefore is painful.
Electrolysis: For facial hair, the area around the nipple (but not the pigmented area), stomach and the bikini line.	Electrolysis works in two ways - in a system called 'short-wave diathermy' the heat seals off the blood supply to the hair at the root. 'Galvanic' current uses a chemical reaction to destroy the hair root. 'The Blend' method combines the two. It has to be carried out over a period of time because you need to treat the hair during the active growing stage. Regrowth is slow during treatment. Hormonal changes during the life cycle may cause new growth.	You need to accept from the start that electrolysis can be a very lengthy, and therefore expensive, business. The Blend method is considered the most effective. Puffiness and redness can occur afterwards. You should keep the skin clean, not wear fragranced body lotions or moisturisers, or sun lotion and avoid excessive heat for 24 hours afterwards. Washing in tepid water and applying diluted antiseptic lotion can help to avoid small spots. Check that the operator is highly-experienced as scarring can occur if the needle is inserted incorrectly. Tweezer methods of electrolysis are available for salon and home use and are reported to be variable in their efficacy.

HAIR

Gleaming, glossy
and stronger than a
piece of copper wire of
the same dimension,
healthy hair is
traffic-stopping hair.

HAIR TIPS

Strong, healthy hair should be able to stretch by 25 per cent.
You can test this by taking a hair and measuring its length along a ruler.
Now stretch the hair up the ruler until it breaks.
If it stretches by less than 25 per cent, your hair is dry or damaged.

• Our hair grows about 2cm a month, we shed 100-150 hairs a day and each hair has a lifespan of 8 years.

• Precise, short styles need cutting every 4 weeks; other hairstyles need a trim every 6 weeks.

• Although the hair is dead, apart from the cells at the root, moisture, protein and other ingredients can enter the hair shaft through its outer, fish-like scales, called cuticles.

• There is no harm in washing your hair every day, providing you treat it gently and use high quality shampoos. If you live in a polluted environment, trichologists positively recommend it.

• Hair is very susceptible to breakage when it is wet. Use a wide-toothed comb or afro comb (which are saw-cut so there are no sharp edges) on wet hair. If your hair has tangled, comb out a small section of the hair at a time, starting at the ends and gradually working up the hair shaft towards the roots. To avoid tangling long hair while shampooing and conditioning, don't pile the hair on top of your head. Work your fingers gently through the length of the hair as you wash it.

• Over-brushing can be detrimental to your hair.

• Conditioning the hair smooths down the hair cuticles. Light then reflects off the surface better, giving hair its shine.

• A final rinse with water as cold as you can stand gives hair a sheen for the same reason. Always rinse in clean water, as soap residues can dull the hair.

• Blot - don't rub - the hair, with a towel in order to avoid ruffling up the cuticle.

• Blow-dry on a warm setting, always working down the hair shaft. Dry small sections at a time. Don't blow-dry hair when it is sopping wet.

• Use a 'vent' brush, which has holes in the base, pressing the hair flat against it and holding the hairdryer close to the brush.

• Do not hold the dryer against the hair for longer than a few seconds and keep it moving.

• Be aware that permanent colourants and perms alter the protein structure of the hair. Your hair will no longer be so resilient and will require regular deep-conditioning treatments to maintain moisture levels.

• The sun damages the hair's protein. Wind, chlorine and salt water all open up the cuticle and allow moisture to escape. Look out for hair protectors that contain sun filters, always rinse out sea and swimming pool water thoroughly and use after-sun and anti-chlorine shampoos and conditioners.

We frequently ask our hairdresser for a dramatically shorter style
when we have split from a loved one. Cutting the hair symbolises a fresh start.

GREASY HAIR

Greasy hair can be inherited, due to your hormones
or low sulphur levels in the blood, or caused by
over-stimulation of the sebaceous glands.
So what can you do to dry it up?

• Wash your hair every day with lukewarm water, using a high quality, frequent wash shampoo. Some greasy hair shampoos contain more detergent, which can leave the rest of your hair stripped of the hair's natural, protective oils. Alternatively, specialist oily scalp treatment shampoos are available, which don't dry out the ends. These vary between shampoos which can be used continuously and those designed to be used occasionally.

• When shampooing, try to massage the hair gently with the palm of the hand, not the fingertips, to avoid stimulating the oil glands.

• Anti-dandruff shampoos can make the hair greasy if used excessively.

• Keep conditioners, which may contain oils, away from the roots.

• Finish with a cold rinse (if you can bear to) to help close the pores on the scalp.

• Waxes and pomades are usually too heavy for greasy hair. Try not to use too much of any styling product, or you will make your hair lank. Mousses which contain alcohol can be useful when used at the roots, as alcohol has a drying action.

• Try not to brush, comb or touch your hair too frequently.

• Wash combs and brushes frequently to avoid transferring grease, dust and dirt to your hair.

DRY, DAMAGED HAIR

Does your hair sometimes feel and look like straw, or would a haystack be a better description? Dry hair is vulnerable hair and calls for a little extra love and attention.

• Dry hair is thirsty. It wants more moisture and is vulnerable to losing the moisture it does have.

• Your hair may be naturally dry because your sebaceous glands produce less of the hair's protective oil, or because your hair is curly and the oil tends to stay at the roots. More often, hair is dry because of the way we treat it: chemical treatments, over-using heated styling equipment and not conditioning the hair enough are prime culprits.

• Remoisturising shampoos will help to improve the condition of dry hair.

• You must condition your hair after every wash. Conditioning seals the outer 'scales' of the hair and prevents moisture from escaping. Gently massage the conditioner in with your fingertips, rather than just dolloping it on, and then comb it through with a wide-toothed comb. This helps the active ingredients to penetrate the hair cuticles, rather than just sitting on top of them. Leave-in conditioners are also good for dry hair, especially for very dry ends.

• Intensive conditioners make an immediate difference to dry hair and should be used weekly.

• Chlorine, saltwater, sunlight and wind all spell disaster for dry hair. Applying deep-conditioning protein packs to the hair twice a week before you go on holiday will give your hair a head start.

• Sun and swim protective gels and lotions, which have sun filters, are important for dry hair and some give day-long protection from chlorine. If you have long hair, wear it in a ponytail or a chignon to reduce the surface area exposed to the elements.

• The great majority of people who use hairdryers overdry their hair. Bear in mind that you could be frying your hair: hairdryers commonly reach temperatures of 80°C and some have been shown to overheat to 200°C. Always keep the hairdryer moving, with the nozzle pointing down the hair shaft to keep the cuticles flat, and check occasionally that the coils are not glowing red hot. Programmable hairdryers, which contain microchips to regulate the temperature, are available. Apply a safety shield to your hair by spritzing on a heat-resistant lotion before you switch on. Some of these lotions also contain hair strengthening ingredients.

• The moisturising ingredient pro-vitamin B5, which is also known as panthenol, is now widely used in shampoos and conditioners. It is particularly good for dry hair, although it is also useful for other hair types. Due to its small molecule size, it is able to penetrate the hair.

• Dry hair is very brittle. Use styling mousses that are alcohol-free (alcohol is very drying). If your hair is prone to be dull, do not use mousse every day as the styling resins it contains can make it duller.

• Do not use tongs, crimping or straightening irons if you can avoid them.

• Centrally-heated and air-conditioned offices frequently have desert-dry atmospheres and will steal the moisture from your hair, just as they do from your skin. Glossers, styling gels and serums, used sparingly, will provide a barrier to moisture loss.

• Remember that perms and permanent 'tints' affect the hair structure and that by repeating a perm or tint every four months or so, you are chemically-treating hair that is already weakened. Use conditioners with strengthening properties.

FRIZZY HAIR

Frizziness can affect straight hair as well as curly hair and controlling it can be a beauty nightmare.

• Frizzy hair is always dry. It may also be damaged, because dry hair is fragile. Your hair may be naturally dry, or have become dry as a result of chemical processes such as perming, highlighting or colouring, or through the use of heated styling appliances.

• You can have an oily scalp, but dryness and frizziness along the length of the hair. Treat them, as far as possible, with separate hair products.

• Check that your styling lotions or gels don't contain alcohol, which will dry the hair out further. Beware of mousse which can give curly hair too much volume. Use a blow-dry lotion to protect the hair, and keep the heat setting as low as possible.

• Curly hair is more prone to be frizzy because the hair's protective oils are not distributed efficiently along the hair shaft, and the hair's protective outer cuticles open up where the hair kinks.

• Frizziness is not necessarily restricted only to curly hair, however. Split ends on straight hair can create frizzy flyaways.

• Shampoos and conditioners formulated for dry hair may be suitable, but not if you have fine, frizzy hair because they can weigh the hair down. In this case, experiment with products for fine hair and with shampoos, conditioners and styling lotions formulated especially for frizzy hair, which contain silicone to smooth the hair shaft and seal in moisture.

• If a perm goes frizzy, return to the salon to check if you are drying and styling it correctly. However, it may have been over-processed.

• Damp weather can mean that frizzy hair goes way out of control, with the extra moisture swelling the volume of the hair. Applying styling serums and conditioners before you go outside will help to avoid this.

Hair serums are silky liquids which can dramatically improve the appearance and texture of frizzy hair. They should be applied very sparingly after shampooing and before styling. Gently blot some of the excess moisture from your hair, but don't rub or you will disturb the cuticle and make the hair even more frizzy. Pump or pour a few drops of the serum into your hand and rub your palms together. Smooth your hands down the length of the hair and then distribute the serum with a wide-toothed comb or your fingers. If you have curly hair, do not brush or comb your hair after the initial comb-through while it is drying in order to ensure your curls stay defined, instead of becoming frizzy. These serums contain silicone, which has earnt a reputation for building up the hair. Use a deep cleansing shampoo occasionally should your hair become dull and tell your hairdresser which shampoos, conditioners and styling products you use if you are having a perm or colour.

FINE HAIR

It's wispy, it's hard-to-handle and if you were born with it, you have to learn to live with it. Here's how you can work at the relationship.

• Fine hair relates to the amount of the amino acid, cystine, in the hair and grows out of small follicles.

• Regular haircuts help to prevent split ends, and therefore potential damage to the hair. Blunt cuts work well on very fine hair, although if you have a lot of fine hair, a graduated cut will give the illusion of volume.

• Choose a volumising shampoo, ideally one that also has anti-static properties, to help tame flyaway ends.

• Conditioners can help to thicken the hair, but a product that is too heavy will make the hair limp. Use conditioners specifically formulated for fine hair and apply them sparingly or on the ends only. Most of us tend to use far more of a haircare product than we really need.

• Be sure not to brush your hair when it is wet. Use a good quality, wide-toothed comb instead.

• Thickening lotions and body-building sprays pump up the volume of fine hair. Take care not to overload the hair and spray from at least six inches away. They will help to lift the hair away from the roots. Scrunch dry around the hairline and scalp as your hair dries, using your hands. Hairdryers that have directional combs attached can help.

• Fine hair needs just the minimum of heat when you are drying or styling it. Apply a heat-protective spray first. Some contain panthenol (pro-vitamin B5) and can thicken the hair by up to ten per cent. Protein sprays, known as 'liquid hair' are also effective.

• Hair colourants and highlighting give the impression of thicker hair, particularly if you introduce a variety of tones into the hair. Ask a hairdresser's advice.

• Perming swells the hair shaft and can give added body. But it must be done carefully, as fine hair is fragile.

HAIR THINNING AND LOSS

If you notice signs of thinning, wider hair partings or your hair is coming out in greater than normal quantities, you should investigate the possible causes.

Hormonal/genetic: In about 30 per cent of women, there are signs of genetic hair loss. Circulating hormones (androgens) can result in thinner hair shafts, wider partings and hair loss. To correct this problem, a trichologist may need to work with a hormone specialist. Some oral contraceptives have an 'androgenic' effect and should be avoided.

Thyroid: Abnormal thyroid function causes hair loss. In low (hypo-) thyroid conditions, it may take two to three years before hair loss is noticeable. A high (hyper-) thyroid function can produce excessive hair loss within eight to ten weeks. Sudden weight loss can bring hair changes similar to those of hyperthyrodism. Losing a stone in three to four weeks can result in hair being shed around ten weeks later.

Alopecia: This is the generic term for hair loss. 'Alopecia areata' is an auto-immune disorder where the body sees the hair as a foreign body. It is lost in patches and usually grows back of its own accord. In 'alopecia totalis', all hair is lost from the head and eyebrows and does not always regrow. 'Alopecia universalis' affects the whole body.

Nutrition: You should ensure that you eat regularly. Taking excess multivitamins can cause hair problems.

Stress: Tension can prevent absorption of food, and can alter levels of the hormone prolactin. This increases the uptake of the hormone androgen into the cells, which can especially affect those with a tendency to genetic hair loss.

Pregnancy: Hormonal changes extend the usual growth cycle of the hair and as a result, large amounts of hair may then be shed for some time following the birth.

AFRO HAIR

Afro hair is beautiful but headstrong and surprisingly fragile.

It has the tightest curl of any hair type because it grows from a curved hair follicle which causes the hair to twist and kink. Afro hair is more resistant to chemical processes because it has between seven and eleven layers of cuticle scales (the outer protective coating on each hair) as against only four to seven on Caucasian hair. Additionally, the inner layer, or cortex, has less volume which means that chemicals will process more quickly than on other types of hair.

CONDITIONING

Afro hair needs regular conditioning to keep it supple and healthy, because the hair's natural oil cannot travel down the hair shaft easily. Specialist products contain proteins (often keratin and collagen) to help rebuild the inner structure; Panthenol (part of the vitamin B complex) to give body and gloss, glycerine to attract moisture into the hair shaft and neutral henna to add shine. Oils work by coating the hair, preventing moisture loss whilst adding sheen. Too much, however, will make hair look greasy. Silicones, which are included in many conditioners, cover hair with a protective polymer which remains on the hair even after rinsing. Some manufacturers recommend the use of heat to aid penetration of a particular product. Use hot towels to form a turban and leave for the time specified. Do not be tempted to accelerate the result by using a hand dryer as this can lead to scalp irritation.

RELAXING

Straightening or reducing the curl in afro hair can make it more manageable and easy to style, but the process is drastic as the chemicals change the inner hair structure. The result is permanent, only disappearing as the hair grows. Relaxers come in varying strengths to suit different hair textures and the results required. On longer hair, the weight helps maintain the straightened look for longer. Relaxed hair should not be combed - it can take the elasticity right out, causing hair to snap off. Instead, use a good quality bristle brush and a gentle action.

PERMING

Wet-look or curly perms, curl re-directors and soft curl perms give a permanent looser curl to afro hair. To prevent frizziness and maintain curl definition special curl activators and moisturising sprays can be used. Hair that has been previously relaxed, bleached or treated with a colour restorer (one containing metallic salts) should not be permed. It is always advisable to do a strand test on a lock of hair first.

HOT PRESSING COMBS

One of the simplest ways of temporarily straightening afro hair is to use hot pressing combs. The disadvantage is that as soon as the hair is exposed to moisture it reverts back to its original shape. To prevent damage, use a pressing oil or cream to protect the hair. Coarse, wiry hair is difficult to press while medium texture hair responds well. Fine hair needs the most care since it burns and breaks easily. When pressing short hair take care or you could burn the scalp. Bleached, tinted, grey or lightened hair can be discoloured by the intense heat.

CARING FOR AFRO HAIR

• Use a wide-toothed, smooth-ended afro comb to gently 'rake' through your hair.

• Scalp massage stimulates the circulation and encourages sebum production and distribution of oil along the length of the hair.

• When relaxing, perming or colouring afro hair always follow the directions supplied with the product and do a strand or skin sensitivity test.

• When washing afro hair, lather only once using a tiny amount of shampoo and rinse hair thoroughly in warm water. Blot dry, don't rub, before applying conditioner. Wet hair stretches - particularly if it has been chemically treated - and can easily be damaged by rough handling when drying or styling.

• Pomades and gels are good for moulding afro hair. Choose non-greasy formulas that give hair a healthy shine.

• Don't plait or weave afro hair too tightly. If hair is pulled forcibly, too often, it can disrupt the hair follicles and cause scar tissue to form, leading to hair loss.

HAIR COLOURING

It's simple, it's fast and it makes you look and feel good.
Colouring your hair makes a statement about your personal style.

One in three women colour their hair and a remarkable 14 million applications of permanent hair colourants are used each year.

Today's pigments have a new translucency, so instead of getting a block of matte, solid colour your hair's natural tonal variation is mimicked in the new shade. Some people may have an allergic reaction so a skin test should be done prior to use.

Temporary colours include gels, mousses, shampoos, sprays and paints. They contain large colour molecules that adhere to the outside or cuticle layer of the hair.

The effect washes away within one to six shampoos unless the hair is particularly porous, when some remnants of colour will remain. The reason temporary colours don't wash off in the rain is because dye particles are bound together by a polymer and this is resistant to humidity or damp, climatic conditions. Temporary colour will not lighten hair or cover grey but will remove brassy tones from white or blonde hair. Good when a quick, but fleeting, change is wanted. Ideal to help maintain colour intensity between applications of semi or permanent colourants.
Processing time: 2-3 minutes.*

Semi-permanent liquids, creams and mousses enrich or darken hair, but cannot make it lighter. Good for intensifying tone, covering the first few grey hairs and adding gloss. Semi-permanents contain small colour molecules that enter through the cuticle and adhere to the outer edge of the cortex, allowing the colour to last for around eight shampoos - a little colour washing out each time. They are ideal when you want to experiment with colour without committing yourself.
Processing time: 5-30 minutes.*

Longer-lasting semi-permanent liquids, creams, mousses and sticks. A cross between semis and permanents, they contain peroxide, which enables the small molecules to penetrate even deeper into the cortex, so they last longer (up to 21 shampoos). They can't lighten, but will brighten and enrich the hair adding colour and shine. Suitable for covering grey. Continued use results in slight regrowth.
Processing time: 10-30 minutes.*

Permanent or tint cream formulations that are mixed with peroxide before use. They can lighten or darken any hair colour and effectively cover grey. The small colour molecules enter the cortex and expand, becoming too large to escape. Colour will not wash out or fade significantly and has to grow out with your hair. Roots need retouching every six weeks. When treating regrowth it is important not to overlap previously treated hair or you will get a build-up of colour on mid-lengths to ends. Ideal when you are sure of your colour choice. As with semi-permanent colours, a skin test prior to use is essential and a strand test is important.
Processing time: 30-45 minutes.*

MORE HAIR COLOURING

Vegetable colour contains natural pigment together with adhesive polymers or resins which stick to the cuticle of the hair to add colour whilst smoothing each strand. The result is colour enhancement with shine. Gives good coverage of up to 80 per cent of grey. Colour washes away in around six to eight shampoos. Processing time: 10-30 minutes.*

Henna is obtained from the dried leaves of the Egyptian privet, Lawsonia Alba, which is harvested, dried and the leaves crushed into a green powder. Henna adds shine and body to the hair as well as a range of subtle reddish hues. Shade variations are achieved by mixing henna with herbs such as camomile or sage. Natural henna, which is used for conditioning rather than colour, comes from the crushed root of the plant. Henna is a coating dye, meaning that it stains the hair shaft by adhering to the cuticle or outer layer. The degree of staining depends on how porous that hair is and how long the henna is left on. The colour fades gradually so subsequent applications (every six to eight weeks) are needed to keep the colour intense. The result you achieve depends on your natural hair colour. Henna applied to brunette or black hair produces a warm, reddish glow, while lighter hair goes a beautiful reddish gold.

Henna does not lighten hair and is not suitable for use on blonde hair or hair that is more than 20 per cent grey, white, tinted or bleached or highlighted, as it will only produce an unnatural orange. Henna, even if not visible to the naked eye, remains in the hair until it grows out and can cause some subsequent problems with perming or chemical colouring. Henna will stain skin and nails, so always wear rubber gloves and smear a barrier cream round the hair line and ears to prevent staining. Processing time: one to two hours - branded henna mixes are often less (some Indian women leave henna on for 24 hours anointing the head with oils to keep the paste supple).*

Bleach liquid, cream, powder or gel is the most drastic way to alter hair colour as it strips pigment from the hair creating a white/blonde effect. This is the only way to change very dark hair to very pale. Regrowth is rapid, so roots need regular retouching - every three to four weeks. Damage to the cuticle may result from over-bleaching and the hair may be left spongy and porous with a tendency to retain moisture. Bleaching may even cause the hair to break off, so bleached hair needs regular intensive conditioning treatments. Best for short hair. Processing time: 15-60 minutes.

* Processing times given are as a guide only and should always be double checked with the manufacturers' instructions.

COLOUR CARE

Treating coloured hair carefully is crucial.
Follow the tips here:

• Don't colour hair that is split or damaged, or that has been bleached or hennaed - consult a professional and tell them exactly what you have used. Permed hair can be coloured as long as it is in good condition.

• Always do a strand and skin sensitivity test.

• The longer you leave the colour on your hair the more vivid the end result will be. If your hair is dry or porous remember that it will soak up colour more quickly.

• When retouching the roots of tinted or bleached hair, apply new colour only to the regrowth area. Any overlap will result in an uneven colour.

• Avoid colouring hair if you are taking prescribed drugs as the chemical balance of your hair can alter.

• Artificial colour is broken down by oxygen. Every day, the oxygen in the air is in contact with hair, slowly causing the colour to fade. Other influences like strong wind, chlorinated water (which contains high levels of oxygen), salt water, perspiration and sun all conspire to speed up fading. To maintain your colour as long a possible you should:

• Protect hair from the sun's rays by wearing a hat or using a protective lotion.

• Use shampoos and conditioners formulated for coloured hair. After shampooing, gently towel-dry your hair - do not rub vigorously as this ruffles the cuticles and allows colour to escape. Use a conditioner every time you shampoo and treat your hair to an intensive conditioning treatment once a month.

HIGHLIGHTS

Highlights are created when fine sections of the hair are lightened to give a sun-kissed effect. The colour commitment is less than that of all-over permanent colour as regrowth is not so obvious and the roots will only need re-doing every 3-4 months. Best for dark blonde to mid-brown hair. It can be tricky when home highlighting to get the colour right to the roots and sometimes seepage occurs through the holes in the cap, giving a blotchy result. Hairdressers weave out strands of hair with a tail comb, which enables them to control exactly which hair is to be treated, and they can vary the colours to give a more natural effect. This process is time consuming and accounts for the price differential between home and salon highlights. Lowlights are the opposite to highlights, with colours that are darker or warmer than your natural colour, added to give depth and definition to a style.

IF THINGS GO WRONG

Most home colourant manufacturers have a consumer help line to call in case you have difficulties. If the advice you are given doesn't solve the problem don't try applying more colour. Visit a salon and tell them exactly what you have used and how long you left it on your hair. The more information you can give, the more chance they have of rectifying the situation without damaging your hair.

P E R M I N G

Cleopatra used twigs and clay and then baked her hair in the sun to produce curls. Today, life is a little easier.

It is now possible to add root lift, waves, texture, volume and curls whilst maintaining the condition of your hair. Advanced formulations mean there are lotions designed for bleached, coloured, tinted or hard to curl hair and variants that can be used on previously permed hair. Tell your stylist whether you want to let your hair dry naturally, or use a dryer or heated roller to achieve your finished style. A professional perm should only be prescribed after careful analysis of your hair type and condition and discussion about the look you want to achieve.

HOW PERMS WORK
Waving lotions work by breaking down the bonds in the inner structure of the hair so they can be reshaped by winding onto rods or rollers. Once processing is complete the new shape is set by applying a neutraliser which reforms the bonds to give a permanent wave or curl.

Perms are only suitable for hair that is in good condition. Very dry or damaged hair is generally not strong enough to withstand the chemicals used in perms and can end up at best frizzy, at worse broken and split. It is also not advisable to use perm lotions if you suffer from any scalp disorder or have eczema or psoriasis.

SALON SOLUTIONS
Professional perm lotions are selected by the hairdresser to suit your hair. They include acid waves for fine, sensitive or fragile hair; alkaline perms which give firm curl results on normal or hard to perm hair and 'exothermic' perms which are heat activated and are often used when a more conditioned, bouncy result is wanted. The different types of perm can be used with a variety of techniques for varying results and this is where hairdressers have the upper hand. A body perm adds volume and soft movement using large rods or rollers. Root perms can give lift, height and fullness at the root area only. Spiral perms can be used to create tumbling curls on long hair. Spot perms are used when just one area, for example the sides or fringe, needs movement or lift. Finally, texture can be created using a weave perm which involves perming certain

sections and leaving the remaining hair straight to give natural-looking body and bounce.

HOME PERM TIPS
If you decide to use a home perm be sure to choose a formula that suits your hair type. It is possible to buy home perm lotions for coloured and difficult-to-curl hair. Boxes are also labelled with the type of curl you can expect to achieve, for example, bouncy curls, body, volume or wave. Test curls are most important - don't skip this vital step. The strength and longevity of your perm will depend on the product used, the size of the curls, the length of time the waving lotion is left on and the condition of the hair prior to perming.

- Enlist a friend to help with winding.

- The smaller the rod, the tighter the curl result.

- Rinse, rinse and rinse away the neutraliser after processing - some salons allow water to flow through the hair for 15 minutes to ensure all residues are removed.

CARING FOR CURLS
- Avoid shampooing a perm for 48 hours - it gives the reformed bonds in the hair time to harden and settle into their new shape.

- Use perm-friendly shampoos and conditioners that are designed for curl maintenance.

- After washing hair, gently squeeze out excess water and detangle using a wide-toothed comb.

- Dry permed hair naturally or use your dryer on a gentle heat/speed setting with a diffuser attachment if possible.

- If humid weather makes your curls temporarily droop, spritz with water and then scrunch with your hands to re-activate the curls. Gels, styling wax and serums help with separation.

BEAUTY BU

ALPHA HYDROXY ACIDS Also called AHAs and sometimes "fruit acids", they are a group of acids found in fruits and foods which are effective in increasing skin cell renewal and exfoliating the top layer of the skin, reducing the appearance of fine lines and generally improving the texture of the skin. AHAs can also be produced in the laboratory.

ANTIOXIDANTS These ingredients can have two purposes. They can help to protect a product from deterioration and the term is also used to describe ingredients which help to prevent free radicals from damaging the skin.

BIOTECHNOLOGY The process by which a nature-identical ingredient is manufactured in the laboratory.

BROAD SPECTRUM SUNSCREEN Sun filters which offer some protection against ultraviolet light across both the UVA and UVB wavelengths.

CERAMIDES These are lipids (oils) naturally found in the outer layers of the skin. They can be included in skincare products to reinforce the skin's natural barrier, giving added cohesion to cell layers.

COLLAGEN The protein fibres found in the dermis of the skin. An animal-derived ingredient also used in some moisturisers to help soften the appearance of fine lines.

DERMATOLOGICALLY TESTED A product which has been tested on the skin of human volunteers, under controlled conditions approved by a dermatologist, to monitor it for any signs that it may cause irritation. These panels also tend to include sensitive-skinned individuals, thereby ensuring the lowest possible risk of causing irritation.

DERMIS Also known as the connective tissue, the dermis is the layer of skin found beneath the epidermis and is where collagen and elastin lie.

ELASTIN Elastic fibres found in the dermis that can become slacker over time due to the effects of the sun, smoking or other causes of premature ageing and due to the ageing process itself.

ENZYMES Enzymes are present in our cells to facilitate biochemical reactions that take place there. They are included in skincare products to improve skin functions or to block certain skin ageing processes.

EPIDERMIS The outermost section of the skin, which consists of layers of cells that have arrived at the surface from the lower levels and which subsequently fall or are rubbed off.

EXFOLIATING Also known as skin sloughing, the process by which you can remove the loose skin cells to improve light reflection and so help the complexion look brighter and smoother. Exfoliation also allows moisturising and active ingredients to act more effectively.

FREE RADICALS Molecules which play a major role in the ageing of the skin by damaging the structure of cells. May be generated on the skin by the action of sunlight, smoking and some atmospheric pollutants.

GLYCOLIC ACID An Alpha Hydroxy Acid that is either synthetically produced or derived from sugar cane.

HYPO-ALLERGENIC A product designed to minimise the risk of allergic reaction by using only ingredients shown to have a safe history of use.

INFRA-RED Sun rays which we feel on the skin as heat and that have been shown to produce low level damage over a long period of time.

JOJOBA OIL A rich, natural lubricant obtained from the seeds of a native Mexican shrub. Good for treating dry skin and scalps and often used in lipsticks.

KELP EXTRACT A seaweed that can help stimulate, soothe and refresh the skin.

LANOLIN A very lubricating and softening skin moisturiser obtained from sheeps' wool.

ZZ  WORDS

LIGHT DIFFUSING Particles included in skincare and make-up products that scatter the light reflected off the skin, creating a soft focus effect on lines and wrinkles.

LIPOSOMES Minute fluid-filled spheres that contain active ingredients which can help to hold back the skin ageing process. They can penetrate in between the cells of the outer layers of the skin.

MELANIN Naturally present in the skin, melanin is triggered by sunlight to provide protection against harmful ultraviolet rays

NON-COMEDOGENIC Refers to a product that has been shown not to block the pores, which can cause blackheads (comedones) or spots.

ORCHID OIL This is used for its conditioning properties to help maintain your skin's suppleness.

PANTHENOL Also called Pro-Vitamin B5, panthenol attracts moisture to the hair and skin and has a long-lasting hydrating effect.

pH BALANCED The pH scale measures the acidity or alkalinity of a solution with neutral being a pH of 7 and any numbers below showing increasing acidity, and above, increasing alkalinity. Healthy skin is slightly acidic, so "pH balanced" products tend to be acidic in order to maintain the skin's natural "acid mantle", its protective and lubricating film.

PHOTO-AGEING Skin damage as a result of exposure to ultraviolet light.

QUERCITIN Found in the rinds of citrus fruits, it has antioxidant properties and is thought to improve the strength of the skin's capillaries.

RETIN A A product that contains Retinoic Acid, this is a derivative of vitamin A which is a treatment for acne that has also been used for its anti skin-ageing effects. (It should not be used by women who may become pregnant).

SPFs Sun Protection Factors used in sunscreens; they indicate protection afforded from UVB rays and therefore the length of time you can stay in the sun without burning. If you would normally burn within 15 minutes when not wearing a sunscreen, an SPF of 10 gives you 15x10 minutes of protection.

STRATUM CORNEUM Sometimes called the horny layer, this is the surface of the skin.

SWEET BALM EXTRACT A plant extract used for its gentle cleansing qualities.

TEA TREE OIL A natural antiseptic essential oil that is derived from the leaves of Australia's Melaleuca Alternifolia tree.

UVA and UVB Simply explained, these are ultraviolet light rays. UVA rays are known as the ageing rays and UVB rays as the burning rays.

VITAMINS Increasingly being used in moisturisers, anti skin-ageing treatments, sunscreens and colour cosmetics and reputed to help maintain healthy skin. Vitamin A and its relative beta-carotene, Vitamin C and Vitamin E are all antioxidant vitamins.

WHEATGERM Helps to condition the skin and provides Vitamin E.

WITCH HAZEL A plant extract that is soothing and refreshing.

XANTHINES A group of chemicals related to caffeine that is used in some cellulite treatments and are reputed to assist in the combustion of fat. Aminophylline, which is used in a range of cellulite products, is a member of the xanthine family.

YARROW EXTRACT Used for its refreshing and soothing properties.

ZINC OXIDE A filter used in sunscreens to shield the skin from ultraviolet rays.

Further advice

Skincare and make-up advice is available from N°7 Consultants in Boots stores. All N°7 Consultants are specially trained and have extensive product knowledge, so that they can recommend the best products for your needs.

The following organisations can supply further information and, where applicable, details of trained members in your area on receipt of a large stamped addressed envelope:

The Acne Support Group
PO Box 230
Hayes, Middlesex UB4 9HW

The British Association of Beauty Therapy and Cosmetology
Parabola House
Parabola Road
Cheltenham
Gloucester GL50 3AH

The Cellulite Clinic
London College of Massage
5-6 Newman Passage
London W1 3PF
Telephone: 0171-637 7125

The National Eczema Society
163 Eversholt Street
London NW1 1BU
Telephone: 0171-388 4097

The British Reflexology Association
Monks Orchard
Whitbourne
Worcester WR6 5RB
Telephone: 01886 821207

The International Federation of Aromatherapy
Stamford House
2-4 Chiswick High Road
London W4 1TH
Telephone: 0181-742 2605 (SAE + £2)

Institute of Trichology
228 Stockwell Road
London SW9 9SU
Telephone: 0171-733 2056

The Society of Teachers of the Alexander Technique
20 London House
266 Fulham Road
London SW10 9EL
Telephone: 0171-351 0828

Author's Acknowledgements

The author expresses grateful thanks for their time and expertise to:

Delwyn Mallett of Delwyn Mallett Design Associates; The Development Team, Boots Contract Marketing and members of the Boots Personal Care Business Centre; Helen Bowering of N°7; Claire Attenborough and Lisa Brand of Attenborough Associates; Lisa Eveleigh of A.P. Watt; Di Lewis of Bookings; Stephen Parker of Boss Models London; Linda McLean; Anita Grossman of A&R; Aimee Adams; Rebecca Barnes; Jocelyn Bailey; Jibby Beane; Pauline Brown; Jane Campsie; Sheila Carton; James Dodds; Simon Emmett; Pasquale Ferrante; Colin Gold; Lisa Gorman; Nicola Hall, Chairman of the British Reflexology Association; Daniel Galvin; Tiggy Gee and Fiona Simon of G.S.M.; John Gladwin; Ruby Hammer; Julia Harris of BABTAC; Derek Henderson; Caroline Hogg; Barry Hollywood; John Hudson; Debbie Hyams; David Lambert; Deseree Lederer; Vincenzo Liberato and Jules of Elite Premier; Adele Lovell; Dr. Nicholas Lowe; Dr. Vivian Lunny, Chairperson of the International Federation of Aromatherapists; Anthony and Jill Malkin; Russ Malkin; John Painell; Chloe Mallett; Bryan Marryshow; Adam Melli; Michel and Myriam Momy; Clare Park; Fiona Parkhouse; Erika Pek of 2 Management; Janine Phillipson; Lindsay Cruickshank of Premier Plus; Lee Pycroft; Sara Raeburn; Edina and Shebah Ronay; Dr. Hugh Rushton; Carole Ann Sellicks; Sam Stafford; Trudi Smith; Beverley Streeter of Streeters; Terrie Tanaka; Francesca Taylor; Catherine Turner; Michael Van Clarke of Michael Van Clarke hairdressers; Karen Ford, Tori Edwards, Jane Wood and Ellis of Models One; Clare Castagnetti, Michelle Anderson and Richard Habberley of Select; Jacki Wadeson; Nikki Whelan; Mary Wiles; Paul Windle of Windle hairdressers; James Sawyer, Sarah Creighton-Howes, Sarah Molden, Edward Sibley, Barry Morgan of J&A Artwork Ltd.

Clothes and accessories kindly supplied by:

Astuces; Austin Reed; Edina Ronay; French Connection; Alchemy, Sub-Couture and Vicky Martin at Hyper Hyper; Jeffrey Rogers; Next; Pineapple Dance Centre; Ronald Joyce; Ronit Zilkha; Russell and Bromley; Tatters at Harrods; Waterman; Whistles

Copper bath and accessories: The Water Monopoly (0171-624 2636)

Photographs by:
The Three Graces by Peter Paul Rubens (1577-1640) Prado, Madrid/Bridgeman Art Library, London - 130
Camera Press - 32
Simon Emmett - 46, 54, 57, 61, 62, 66
John Gladwin - Cover: 31, 44, 69, 77, 78, 81, 82, 84, 122, 136, 140, 159. Back Cover:
Derek Henderson - 10, 18, 21, 25, 26, 27, 29, 42, 46, 80, 86, 87, 89, 90, 117, 119, 142, 154, 156, 162
Barry Hollywood - 52, 53, 76, 79, 83, 85, 99, 101, 102, 105, 106, 152, 161
John Hudson - 6
Kobal Collection - 95, 145
Delwyn Mallett - 40, 50, 58, 65, 75, 138, 146
Michel Momy - 12, 14, 16, 23, 70, 73, 108, 110, 112, 115, 121, 124, 127, 132, 134, 149
Paramount (courtesy Kobal Collection) - 92
Transworld/Anna/Piccardi - 34
Transworld/Blonde - 39
Universal (courtesy Kobal Collection) - 151